THE
SHURLEY
METHOD

ENGLISH MADE EASY

LEVEL 2

Student Workbook

By
Brenda Shurley
Ruth Wetsell

Shurley Instructional Materials, Inc., Cabot, Arkansas

03-05
Second Edition
ISBN 1-881940-64-0 (Level 2 Student Workbook)

1 2   3   4   5   6   7   8   9   10   05 04 03 02 01 00 99 98 97

PRETEST—PATTERN 1

Exercise 1: Tell how each word is used in the sentences by writing the part of speech above the word. Example: **N** for noun, **Adj** for adjective, **Adv** for adverb, etc.

1. The frightened little rabbit ran away quickly.

2. My father's big clock ticked loudly on the wall.

3. I laughed at my dad's funny clown suit.

4. What are the Adjective Questions? _____

5. What are the Adverb Questions? _____

Exercise 2: Put capital letters and marks of punctuation as needed in the sentences below.

6. last week joe went to dallas texas

7. i want sam to help me find mr williams

8. did aunt ruth say that uncle tom was born on may 20 1965

Exercise 3: Write **S** for a complete sentence or **F** for a sentence fragment on the line beside each group of words.

_____ 9. The boats sailed around the lake.   _____ 11. The angry panther in the jungle.

_____ 10. Blew out of the mountains for an hour.   _____ 12. We walked to school.

| Exercise 4: Write **S** for singular or **P** for plural. | |
Noun	S or P
13. gloves	
14. blanket	
15. plates	

| Exercise 5: Write **C** for common or **P** for proper. | |
Noun	C or P
16. Oklahoma	
17. turkey	
18. Mr. West	

Exercise 6: Underline the complete subject once and the complete predicate twice.

19. The five beavers worked quickly.   20. The big elephants walked through the jungle.

Exercise 7: Underline the simple subject once and the simple predicate twice.

21. The geese flew for hours.   22. The little kittens played with the yarn.

Exercise 8: On the back of this pretest, write a paragraph on this topic: "What I Think About English."

What I Think About English

UNIT 1: GROUP 1 (KINDS OF SENTENCES) TEST

Exercise 1: Write a period **(.)** and the letter **D** for a Declarative sentence. Write a question mark **(?)** and the letters **Int** for an Interrogative sentence.

1. I   went   to   town   yesterday _____

2. Two   raindrops   fell   on   my   head _____

3. My   sister   is   in   the   first   grade _____

4. Did   you   go   to   the   ballgame _____

5. Were   you   at   the   game _____

6. Are   you   going   to   the   party _____

Exercise 2: Underline the correct word to begin each sentence below. Then, write a period **(.)** and the letter **D** for a Declarative sentence. Write a question mark **(?)** and the letters **Int** for an Interrogative sentence.

7. (Sam,   sam)   went   to   the   movies _____

8. (did,   Did)   you   go   to   school   today _____

Sentence Work

Exercise 3: Underline the **syn** if the words are synonyms. Underline the **ant** if the words are antonyms.

1. pretty, ugly	syn ant	3. below, above	syn ant	5. pupils, students	syn ant
2. above, over	syn ant	4. house, home	syn ant	6. awake, asleep	syn ant

Exercise 4: Write the two sentences below on a sheet of paper. Begin each sentence with a capital letter and put an end mark at the end. (**Declarative sentence:** Use a period. **Interrogative sentence:** Use a question mark.)

7. we walked to town

8. do you like cats

Exercise 5: On your paper, write a declarative sentence and an interrogative sentence. Begin each sentence with a capital letter and put an end mark at the end. (**Declarative sentence:** Use a period. **Interrogative sentence:** Use a question mark.)

UNIT 1: GROUP 2 & GROUP 3 TEST

Exercise 1: Classify each sentence. Use **SN** for subject noun and **V** for verb.

1.   Dogs   barked.

2.   Kittens   played.

3.   Wind   blew.

4.   Cars   raced.

5.   Boys   play.

Exercise 2: Classify each sentence. Use **SN** for subject noun, **V** for verb, and **Adv** for adverb.

1.   Dogs   barked   loudly.

2.   Kittens   played   yesterday.

3.   Wind   blew   strongly.

4.   Cars   raced   away.

5.   Boys   play   quietly   today.

```
                         Sentence Work
```

Exercise 3: Underline the **syn** if the words are synonyms. Underline the **ant** if the words are antonyms.

| 1. cruel, mean | syn   ant | 3. weak, strong | syn   ant | 5. under, beneath | syn   ant |
| 2. quit, stop | syn   ant | 4. noisy, quiet | syn   ant | 6. hot, cold | syn   ant |

Exercise 4: Write the two sentences below on a sheet of paper. Begin each sentence with a capital letter and put an end mark at the end. (**Declarative sentence:** Use a period. **Interrogative sentence:** Use a question mark.)

7. that giraffe has a long neck

8. do you want a hotdog

UNIT 1: GROUP 4 TEST

Exercise 1: Classify each sentence. Use **SN** for subject noun, **V** for verb, **Adv** for adverb, and **Adj** for adjective.

1. Excited   dogs   barked   loudly.

2. Four   little   kittens   played   yesterday.

3. Damp   wind   blew   strongly.

4. Two   red   cars   raced   away.

5. Happy   boys   play   quietly   today.

Sentence Work

Exercise 2: Underline the <u>syn</u> if the words are synonyms. Underline the <u>ant</u> if the words are antonyms.

1. long, short	syn ant	3. happy, glad	syn ant	5. found, lost	syn ant
2. select, choose	syn ant	4. nearly, almost	syn ant	6. appears, seems	syn ant

Exercise 3: Write the two sentences below on a sheet of paper. Begin each sentence with a capital letter and put an end mark at the end. (**Declarative sentence:** Use a period. **Interrogative sentence:** Use a question mark.)

7. did you laugh

8. tom played outside

Exercise 4: Write a declarative sentence and an interrogative sentence of your own on a sheet of paper. Begin each sentence with a capital letter and put an end mark at the end. (**Declarative sentence:** Use a period. **Interrogative sentence:** Use a question mark.)

UNIT 1: GROUP 5 TEST

Exercise 1: Classify each sentence. Use **SN** for subject noun, **V** for verb, **Adv** for adverb, **Adj** for adjective, and **A** for article adjective.

1. The   excited   dogs   barked   loudly.

2. The   four   little   black   kittens   played   happily.

3. A   cold,   damp   wind   blew   strongly.

4. The   ten   new   cars   raced   quickly   away.

5. The   happy   little   boys   played   loudly   yesterday.

Sentence Work

Exercise 2: Underline the **syn** if the words are synonyms. Underline the **ant** if the words are antonyms.

1. take, give	syn ant	3. day, night	syn ant	5. bright, shiny	syn ant
2. win, lose	syn ant	4. wealthy, rich	syn ant	6. mistake, error	syn ant

Exercise 3: Write the two sentences below on a sheet of paper. Begin each sentence with a capital letter and put an end mark at the end. (**Declarative sentence:** Use a period. **Interrogative sentence:** Use a question mark.)

7. the train stops here today

8. does this pen work

Exercise 4: Write a declarative sentence and an interrogative sentence of your own on a sheet of paper. Begin each sentence with a capital letter and put an end mark at the end. (**Declarative sentence:** Use a period. **Interrogative sentence:** Use a question mark.)

UNIT 1: GROUP 6 TEST

Exercise 1: Classify each sentence. Use **SN** for subject noun, **V** for verb, **Adv** for adverb, **Adj** for adjective, and **A** for article adjective.

1. Two   pretty   red   candles   burned   brightly.

2. The   green   phone   rang   loudly.

3. A   big   purple   rabbit   hopped   slowly   away.

4. The   funny   circus   clown   waved   merrily.

5. The   cold   white   snow   fell   gently.

Sentence Work

Exercise 2: Underline the **syn** if the words are synonyms. Underline the **ant** if the words are antonyms.

1. gentle, kind   syn   ant   3. sad, unhappy   syn   ant   5. bigger, smaller   syn   ant
2. up, down   syn   ant   4. empty, full   syn   ant   6. closed, open   syn   ant

Exercise 3: For each noun listed below, write **S** for singular or **P** for plural.

Noun	S or P	Noun	S or P	Noun	S or P
7. babies		10. dogs		13. wolves	
8. flower		11. kitten		14. gloves	
9. clowns		12. airplane		15. bed	

Exercise 4: Write the two sentences below on a sheet of paper. Begin each sentence with a capital letter and put an end mark at the end. (**Declarative sentence:** Use a period. **Interrogative sentence:** Use a question mark.)

16. does he sing well

17. the bus left early

Exercise 5: Write a declarative sentence and an interrogative sentence of your own on a sheet of paper. Begin each sentence with a capital letter and put an end mark at the end. (**Declarative sentence:** Use a period. **Interrogative sentence:** Use a question mark.)

UNIT 1: GROUP 7 TEST

Exercise 1: Classify each sentence. Use **SN** for subject noun, **V** for verb, **Adv** for adverb, **Adj** for adjective, and **A** for article adjective.

1. The   large   ship   sailed   smoothly   away.

2. Eight   funny   yellow   ducks   quacked   loudly.

3. Nine   angry   bees   buzzed   around   angrily.

4. The   curious   little   children   peeked   inside.

5. The   four   large   turtles   traveled   slowly.

Sentence Work

Exercise 2: Underline the <u>syn</u> if the words are synonyms. Underline the <u>ant</u> if the words are antonyms.

1. sweet, sour	syn ant	3. giant, huge	syn ant	5. follow, lead	syn ant
2. young, old	syn ant	4. wet, dry	syn ant	6. start, begin	syn ant

Exercise 3: Write **S** for singular or **P** for plural.	
Noun	**S or P**
7. lakes	
8. store	
9. plants	
10. animal	
11. camels	
12. saddle	

Exercise 4: Write **C** for common or **P** for proper.	
Noun	**C or P**
13. girl	
14. Mrs. Smith	
15. Ted	
16. Dallas	
17. city	
18. England	

Exercise 5: Write the sentence below on a sheet of paper. Begin the sentence with a capital letter and put an end mark at the end. (**Declarative sentence:** Use a period. **Interrogative sentence:** Use a question mark.)

19. tom leaves early

Exercise 6: Write a declarative sentence and an interrogative sentence of your own on a sheet of paper. Begin each sentence with a capital letter and put an end mark at the end. (**Declarative sentence:** Use a period. **Interrogative sentence:** Use a question mark.)

UNIT 1: GROUP 8 TEST

Exercise 1: Classify each sentence. Use **SN** for subject noun, **V** for verb, **Adv** for adverb, **Adj** for adjective, and **A** for article adjective.

1. The   tired   little   kittens   yawned   sleepily.

2. One   little   mouse   scampered   away.

3. The   funny   clowns   laughed   loudly.

4. Eight   large   fish   swam   here   yesterday.

Exercise 2: Use Sentence 1 to underline the complete subject once and the complete predicate twice and to complete the table below.

List the Noun Used	List the Noun Job	Singular or Plural	Common or Proper	Simple Subject	Simple Predicate

Sentence Work

Exercise 3: Underline the <u>syn</u> if the words are synonyms. Underline the <u>ant</u> if the words are antonyms.

1. crawled, raced	syn ant	3. rip, tear	syn ant	5. near, far	syn ant
2. small, little	syn ant	4. fat, thin	syn ant	6. rock, stone	syn ant

Exercise 4: Write **S** for singular or **P** for plural.

Noun	S or P
7. nose	
8. bats	
9. floor	
10. grasshopper	
11. spiders	
12. farmer	

Exercise 5: Write **C** for common or **P** for proper.

Noun	C or P
13. ostrich	
14. Smoky	
15. kittens	
16. Red River	
17. Johnson Park	
18. sun	

Exercise 6: Underline the complete subject once and the complete predicate twice.

19. The little puppies growled playfully.

20. Ten large fish swam away.

21. The big yellow bus honked loudly.

22. Four green frogs swam around slowly.

Exercise 7: Underline the simple subject once and the simple predicate twice.

23. A tiny mouse squeaked.

24. The two yellow cars raced wildly.

25. The vegetable soup cooked slowly.

26. Several children swam yesterday.

UNIT 1: GROUP 9 TEST

Exercise 1: Finding One Part of Speech. For each sentence, write **SN** above the subject and **V** above the verb. Underline the word(s) for the part of speech listed to the left of each sentence.

Adjective(s):   1. The   big   black   dog   jumped   up.

Adverb(s):   2. The   brown   bears   lumbered   slowly   away.

Noun(s):   3. Two   silly   kittens   played   happily.

Verb(s):   4. The   little   baby   cried   loudly.

Exercise 2: Use Sentence 2 above to complete the table below.

List the Noun Used	List the Noun Job	Singular or Plural	Common or Proper	Simple Subject	Simple Predicate

Exercise 3: Underline the **syn** if the words are synonyms. Underline the **ant** if the words are antonyms.

5. damp, wet	syn ant	7. fine, good	syn ant	9. slice, piece	syn ant
6. jolly, sad	syn ant	8. old, new	syn ant	10. hard, soft	syn ant

Exercise 4: Write **S** for singular or **P** for plural.

Noun	S or P
11. bird	
12. wings	
13. ducks	
14. chicken	
15. finger	
16. visitors	

Exercise 5: Write **C** for common or **P** for proper.

Noun	C or P
17. grandmother	
18. aunt	
19. Indian	
20. doctor	
21. New York	
22. Beaver Lake	

Exercise 6: Underline the complete subject once and the complete predicate twice.

23. The silver clock ticked loudly.

24. A big green grasshopper hopped quickly away.

25. The show started yesterday.

26. The children whispered softly.

Exercise 7: Underline the simple subject once and the simple predicate twice.

27. Three happy sisters sang yesterday.

28. The silver scissors cut sharply.

29. The gentle wind blew softly.

30. A huge ship sailed away.

UNIT 1: GROUP 10 TEST

Exercise 1: Finding One Part of Speech. For each sentence, write **SN** above the subject and **V** above the verb. Underline the word(s) for the part of speech listed to the left of each sentence.

Adjective(s):   1. A   fat   dog   growled.

Adverb(s):   2. The   zebra   ran   away.

Noun(s):   3. The   yellow   sun   shines   brightly.

Verb(s):   4. A   panther   jumped   high.

Exercise 2: Use Sentence 4 above to complete the table below.

List the Noun Used	List the Noun Job	Singular or Plural	Common or Proper	Simple Subject	Simple Predicate

Exercise 3: Underline the **syn** if the words are synonyms. Underline the **ant** if the words are antonyms.

5. rip, tear	syn ant	7. wild, tame	syn ant	9. hear, listen	syn ant
6. sick, ill	syn ant	8. easy, hard	syn ant	10. fast, slow	syn ant

Exercise 4: Write **S** for singular or **P** for plural.

Noun	S or P
11. jacket	
12. dinner	
13. plates	
14. bike	
15. parties	
16. refrigerator	

Exercise 5: Write **C** for common or **P** for proper.

Noun	C or P
17. United States	
18. flag	
19. American	
20. Mexican	
21. Canada	
22. Dr. Johnson	

Exercise 6: Underline the complete subject once and the complete predicate twice.

23. The little rabbit hopped away.   25. The ball rolled away.

24. The old man limped slowly.   26. The boys laughed loudly.

Exercise 7: Underline the simple subject once and the simple predicate twice.

27. The frightened mouse ran fast.   29. The white snow fell softly.

28. The bats flew silently away.   30. An enormous snake crawled away.

UNIT 1: GROUP 11 TEST

Exercise 1: Finding the topic: Write the name of the topic that best describes what each row of words is about. Choose from these topics: Colors, Sweets, Animals, Seasons, Kitchen Things, or Transportation.

(1)	(2)	(3)
toaster	winter	candy
oven	spring	ice cream
sink	fall	cake
refrigerator	summer	cookies

Exercise 2: Words that support the topic: In each row, cross out the one idea that does not support the underlined topic at the top.

(1) Pets	(2) Shapes	(3) Water
dog	triangle	lake
shark	circle	river
cat	square	hill
bird	pie	ocean
fish	rectangle	pond

Exercise 3: Sentences that support the topic: Read each topic. Then, cross out the one sentence that does not support the topic.

Topic: A Scary-Looking Monster

1. The monster had green hair that covered his body.
2. The monster's red eyes glowed in the dark.
3. My brother likes monster movies.
4. The monster had sharp yellow teeth.

Topic: Signs of Autumn

1. The leaves turn red, yellow, and orange.
2. Autumn and summer are my favorite seasons.
3. The weather turns cooler.
4. Birds begin flying south for the winter.

UNIT 1: GROUP 12 TEST

Exercise 1: Finding the topic: Write the name of the topic that best describes what each row of words is about. Choose from these topics: Horse Things, Clothing, Kitchen, Tools, or Sources of Light.

(1)	(2)	(3)
_____	_____	_____
flashlights	saddle	oven
lamps	stable	refrigerator
lanterns	oats	stove
light bulb	hay	sink

Exercise 2: Words that support the topic: In each row, cross out the one idea that does not support the underlined topic at the top.

(1) Jewelry	(2) Directions	(3) Sports
pool	up	tennis
bracelet	river	sand
necklace	down	baseball
ring	backwards	basketball
earring	across	football

Exercise 3: Sentences that support the topic: Read each topic. Then, cross out the one sentence that does not support the topic.

Topic: A Bird's Nest

1. The bird finds the right tree to build its nest.
2. The bird collects twigs and branches.
3. The bird weaves the twigs and branches into a nest.
4. The bird eats a worm.

Topic: Fishermen's Equipment

1. Fishermen use fishing poles.
2. They keep their supplies in a tackle box.
3. Fishermen eat a big breakfast.
4. Most fishermen use a fishing boat.

UNIT 1 Writing Outline

Use this two-point outline form to guide you as you write a two-point expository paragraph.

Write a topic: _____
Write 2 points about the topic.

1. _____ 2. _____

Sentence #1   Topic sentence (*Use words in the topic and tell how many points will be used.*)

_____

Sentence #2   2-point sentence (*List your 2 points in the order that you will present them.*)

_____

Sentence #3   State your first point in a complete sentence.

_____

Sentence #4   Write a supporting sentence for the first point.

_____

Sentence #5   State your second point in a complete sentence.

_____

Sentence #6   Write a supporting sentence for the second point.

_____

Sentence #7   Concluding sentence (*Restate the topic sentence and add an extra thought.*)

_____

Student Note: Rewrite your seven-sentence paragraph on a sheet of notebook paper. Be sure to indent and use the checklist below to help you edit your paragraph. Make sure you re-read your paragraph several times slowly.

General Checklist: Check the Finished Paragraph	The Two-Point Expository Paragraph Outline
(1) Have you followed the pattern for a 2-point paragraph? (*Indent, topic sentence, 2-point sentence, 2 main points, 2 supporting sentences, and a concluding sentence.*)	Topic 2 points about the topic Sentence #1: **Topic** sentence Sentence #2: A **two-point** sentence
(2) Do you have complete sentences?	Sentence #3: A **first point** sentence
(3) Have you capitalized the first word and put an end mark at the end of every sentence?	Sentence #4: A **supporting** sentence for the first point Sentence #5: A **second point** sentence
(4) Have you checked your sentences for capitalization and punctuation mistakes?	Sentence #6: A **supporting** sentence for the second point Sentence #7: A **concluding** sentence

UNIT 2: GROUP 1 TEST

Exercise 1: Classify each sentence. Use **SN** for subject noun, **V** for verb, **Adv** for adverb, **Adj** for adjective, **A** for article adjective, **P** for preposition, and **OP** for object of the preposition.

1. The   excited   boys   walked   down   the   path.

2. The   children   played   with   the   kittens.

3. Joe   walks   to   school.

4. The   girls   laughed   at   the   puppets.

Sentence Work

Exercise 2: Underline the **<u>syn</u>** if the words are synonyms. Underline the **<u>ant</u>** if the words are antonyms.

1. end, finish	syn ant	3. funny, sad	syn ant	5. country, nation	syn ant
2. small, large	syn ant	4. tiny, small	syn ant	6. early, late	syn ant

Exercise 3: Write **S** for singular or **P** for plural.

Noun	S or P
7. cat	
8. parrots	
9. pencil	
10. cup	
11. glasses	
12. men	

Exercise 4: Write **C** for common or **P** for proper.

Noun	C or P
13. boys	
14. Charles	
15. day	
16. Tuesday	
17. Aunt Sue	
18. mother	

Exercise 5: Underline the complete subject once and the complete predicate twice.

19. The two girls talked for an hour.
20. Seven children played in the park.
21. The leaves rustled gently in the breeze.
22. The sharp knife lay on the table.

Exercise 6: Underline the simple subject once and the simple predicate twice.

23. Eight tiny puppies slept in a pile.
24. The green watermelons grew quickly.
25. Anna painted on the wall.
26. Five shiny boats raced up the river.

UNIT 2: GROUP 2 TEST

Exercise 1: Classify each sentence. Use **SN** for subject noun, **V** for verb, **Adv** for adverb, **Adj** for adjective, **A** for article adjective, **P** for preposition, and **OP** for object of the preposition.

1. _____ The   two   tall   boys   walked   down   the   path.

2. _____ The   young   children   played   with   the   kittens.

3. _____ Joe   walked   to   school   yesterday.

4. _____ The   happy   girls   giggled   at   the   puppets.

Exercise 2: Use Sentence 4 to underline the complete subject once and the complete predicate twice and to complete the table below.

List the Noun Used	List the Noun Job	Singular or Plural	Common or Proper	Simple Subject	Simple Predicate

Sentence Work

Exercise 3: Underline the <u>syn</u> if the words are synonyms. Underline the <u>ant</u> if the words are antonyms.

1. long, short	syn ant	3. weep, cry	syn ant	5. good, bad	syn ant
2. price, cost	syn ant	4. mend, break	syn ant	6. rush, hurry	syn ant

Exercise 4: Write **S** for singular or **P** for plural.

Noun	S or P
7. children	
8. house	
9. flower	
10. mice	

Exercise 5: Write **C** for common or **P** for proper.

Noun	C or P
11. Mississippi	
12. picture	
13. Mr. Lawson	
14. Oak Street	

Exercise 6: Finding One Part of Speech. For each sentence, write **SN** above the subject and **V** above the verb. Underline the word(s) for the part of speech listed to the left of each sentence.

Adjective(s)   15. A rotten apple fell.   Noun(s)   18. The book fell to the floor.

Adverb(s)   16. Raccoons live nearby.   Preposition(s)   19. The girls went to the movie.

Noun(s)   17. Mother sat in the chair.   Verb(s)   20. The clowns danced around.

UNIT 2: GROUP 3 TEST

Exercise 1: Classify each sentence. Use **SN** for subject noun, **V** for verb, **Adv** for adverb, **Adj** for adjective, **A** for article adjective, **P** for preposition, and **OP** for object of the preposition.

1. _____The   four   happy   boys   walked   down   the   path.

2. _____The   quiet   children   played   with   the   kittens.

3. _____Joe   walked   slowly   to   school   yesterday.

4. _____Two   silly   girls   giggled   at   the   puppets.

Exercise 2: Use Sentence 3 to underline the complete subject once and the complete predicate twice and to complete the table below.

List the Noun Used	List the Noun Job	Singular or Plural	Common or Proper	Simple Subject	Simple Predicate

Sentence Work

Exercise 3: Underline the <u>syn</u> if the words are synonyms. Underline the <u>ant</u> if the words are antonyms.

1. shirt, blouse	syn ant	3. sunny, cloudy	syn ant	5. correct, right	syn ant
2. soiled, dirty	syn ant	4. start, finish	syn ant	6. break, crack	syn ant

Exercise 4: Underline the complete subject once and the complete predicate twice.

7. Bill lives across the street.

8. The men listened to the news.

9. The puppies scampered across the street.

10. A tree fell across the fence.

Exercise 5: Underline the simple subject once and the simple predicate twice.

11. A green frog hopped across the stage.

12. The little kittens slept for two hours.

13. A hawk feeds on small birds.

14. The young men ran around the track.

Exercise 6: Finding One Part of Speech. For each sentence, write **SN** above the subject and **V** above the verb. Underline the word(s) for the part of speech listed to the left of each sentence.

Adjective(s)   15. A black bear raced toward the tent.   Noun(s)   18. Billy went to the zoo.

Adverb(s)   16. The goldfish swam around.   Preposition(s)   19. Linda tripped on the skate.

Adjective(s)   17. The big silver jet flew in the sky.   Preposition(s)   20. Brad walked in the mud.

UNIT 2: GROUP 4 TEST

Exercise 1: Classify each sentence. Use **SN** for subject noun, **V** for verb, **Adv** for adverb, **Adj** for adjective, **A** for article adjective, **P** for preposition, and **OP** for object of the preposition.

1. _____Several   boys   walked   carefully   down   the   steep   path.

2. _____The   happy   children   played   with   the   baby   kittens.

3. _____Joe   walked   quickly   to   the   large   school.

4. _____The   happy   family   walked   to   the   sandy   beach.

Exercise 2: Use Sentence 2 to underline the complete subject once and the complete predicate twice and to complete the table below.

List the Noun Used	List the Noun Job	Singular or Plural	Common or Proper	Simple Subject	Simple Predicate

Sentence Work

Exercise 3: Underline the **syn** if the words are synonyms. Underline the **ant** if the words are antonyms.

1. invent, create	syn ant	3. small, large	syn ant	5. tiny, enormous	syn ant
2. best, worst	syn ant	4. aid, help	syn ant	6. strike, hit	syn ant

Exercise 4: Underline the complete subject once and the complete predicate twice.

7. The canoe glides gracefully through the water.   9. The football player ran fast.

8. The snake crawled under a log.   10. The basketball player fell down.

Exercise 5: Underline the simple subject once and the simple predicate twice.

11. A tiny mouse squeaked.   12. The green pencil writes neatly.

Exercise 6: Finding One Part of Speech. For each sentence, write **SN** above the subject and **V** above the verb. Underline the word(s) for the part of speech listed to the left of each sentence.

Adjective(s)   13. The orange pencil belongs to Tom.   Noun(s)   16. A hole was in the blanket.

Adverb(s)   14. Tom ran fast.   Preposition(s)   17. The owl screeched at night.

Adverb(s)   15. The car turned sharply.   Adverb(s)   18. Sarah sings today.

UNIT 2: GROUP 5 TEST

Exercise 1: Classify each sentence. Use **SN** for subject noun, **V** for verb, **Adv** for adverb, **Adj** for adjective, **A** for article adjective, **P** for preposition, and **OP** for object of the preposition.

1. _____A   tiny   baby   slept   in   the   baby   crib.

2. _____The   two   yellow   ducks   walked   by   the   swift   river.

3. _____Jack   raced   to   the   boat.

4. _____Several   women   waited   by   the   open   door.

Exercise 2: Use Sentence 2 to underline the complete subject once and the complete predicate twice and to complete the table below.

List the Noun Used	List the Noun Job	Singular or Plural	Common or Proper	Simple Subject	Simple Predicate

Sentence Work

Exercise 3: Underline the <u>syn</u> if the words are synonyms. Underline the <u>ant</u> if the words are antonyms.

1. close, near	syn ant	3. start, finish	syn ant	5. bashful, shy	syn ant
2. love, adore	syn ant	4. trouble, problem	syn ant	6. full, empty	syn ant

Reference 18: Capitalization Rules

1. Capitalize the first word of a sentence.
2. Capitalize the pronoun I.
3. Capitalize the names of people and the names of pets. (*Joe, Buffy*)
4. Capitalize titles used with people's names and people's initials. (*Mr., Aunt, Dr., J. C.*)
5. Capitalize names of streets, cities, states, and countries. (*Oak Street, Dallas, Texas, France*)
6. Capitalize the days of the week and the months of the year. (*Monday, May*)

Exercise 4: Correct the capitalization mistakes and put the rule number above each correction.

_____ (Rule numbers)

7. my   aunt   mary   and   i   like   to   shop.   **(Editing Guide: 4 capitalization mistakes)**

_____ (Rule numbers)

8. tom   sent   a   letter   to   mr.   sam   brown.   **(Editing Guide: 4 capitalization mistakes)**

UNIT 2: GROUP 6 TEST

Exercise 1: Classify each sentence. Use **SN** for subject noun, **V** for verb, **Adv** for adverb, **Adj** for adjective, **A** for article adjective, **P** for preposition, and **OP** for object of the preposition.

1. _____ The little girl smiled at the tiny kittens.

2. _____ The happy children ran outside.

3. _____ The hungry lion roared loudly during the night.

4. _____ The hungry boys stared at the chocolate cake.

Exercise 2: Use Sentence 4 to underline the complete subject once and the complete predicate twice and to complete the table below.

List the Noun Used	List the Noun Job	Singular or Plural	Common or Proper	Simple Subject	Simple Predicate

---

Sentence Work

Exercise 3: Underline the **syn** if the words are synonyms. Underline the **ant** if the words are antonyms.

1. lean, thin	syn ant	3. top, bottom	syn ant	5. exciting, thrilling	syn ant
2. seem, appear	syn ant	4. work, play	syn ant	6. thin, thick	syn ant

Exercise 4: Correct the capitalization mistakes and put the rule number above each correction. Use the rule numbers found in Reference 18 on page 77 in the Reference section of your book.

_____(Rule numbers)

7. mother and i are going with mrs. smith.   (Editing Guide: 4 capitalization mistakes)

_____(Rule numbers)

8. today mr. walls paid billy and me.   (Editing Guide: 4 capitalization mistakes)

_____(Rule numbers)

9. i like to feed duffy his food.   (Editing Guide: 2 capitalization mistakes)

UNIT 2: GROUP 7 TEST

Exercise 1: Classify each sentence. Use **SN** for subject noun, **V** for verb, **Adv** for adverb, **Adj** for adjective, **A** for article adjective, **P** for preposition, and **OP** for object of the preposition.

1. _____The two busy boys worked in the yard.

2. _____Dave walked slowly into the kitchen tonight.

3. _____The tired horse walked slowly along the dusty trail.

4. _____Three red balloons burst with a tremendous bang.

Exercise 2: Use Sentence 4 to underline the complete subject once and the complete predicate twice and to complete the table below.

List the Noun Used	List the Noun Job	Singular or Plural	Common or Proper	Simple Subject	Simple Predicate

---

Sentence Work

Exercise 3: Underline the **syn** if the words are synonyms. Underline the **ant** if the words are antonyms.

1. purchase, buy	syn ant	3. bend, curve	syn ant	5. tight, loose	syn ant
2. polite, rude	syn ant	4. evil, bad	syn ant	6. fix, mend	syn ant

---

Exercise 4: Correct the capitalization mistakes and put the rule number above each correction. Use the rule numbers found in Reference 18 on page 77 in the Reference section of your book.

_____(Rule numbers)

7. my birthday is next monday.   **(Editing Guide: 2 capitalization mistakes)**

_____(Rule numbers)

8. do you like living in florida or utah?   **(Editing Guide: 3 capitalization mistakes)**

_____(Rule numbers)

9. mr. richard s. long visited with sara.   **(Editing Guide: 5 capitalization mistakes)**

UNIT 2: GROUP 8 TEST

Exercise 1: Classify each sentence. Use **SN** for subject noun, **V** for verb, **Adv** for adverb, **Adj** for adjective, **A** for article adjective, **P** for preposition, and **OP** for object of the preposition.

1. _____ A   wild   parrot   flew   to   the   tall   tree.

2. _____ James   sat   beside   Sarah   today.

3. _____ Tiny   purple   flowers   grew   by   the   narrow   path.

4. _____ A   bubbling   stew   cooked   over   the   hot   fire.

Exercise 2: Use Sentence 2 to underline the complete subject once and the complete predicate twice and to complete the table below.

List the Noun Used	List the Noun Job	Singular or Plural	Common or Proper	Simple Subject	Simple Predicate

---

Sentence Work

Exercise 3: Underline the <u>**syn**</u> if the words are synonyms. Underline the <u>**ant**</u> if the words are antonyms.

1. easy, simple   syn   ant   3. slowly, quickly   syn   ant   5. start, begin   syn   ant
2. loud, soft   syn   ant   4. fast, quick   syn   ant   6. fast, slow   syn   ant

Exercise 4: Correct the capitalization mistakes and put the rule number above each correction. Use the rule numbers found in Reference 18 on page 77 in the Reference section of your book.

_____(Rule numbers)

7. i   live   on   78   south   main   street.   **(Editing Guide: 4 capitalization mistakes)**

_____(Rule numbers)

8. mr.   jackson   found   fluffy   in   a   tree.   **(Editing Guide: 3 capitalization mistakes)**

_____(Rule numbers)

9. i   heard   mr.   coats   calling   for   pinky.   **(Editing Guide: 4 capitalization mistakes)**

UNIT 2: GROUP 9 TEST

Exercise 1: Classify each sentence. Use **SN** for subject noun, **V** for verb, **Adv** for adverb, **Adj** for adjective, **A** for article adjective, **P** for preposition, and **OP** for object of the preposition.

1. _____ The huge spaceships traveled through space.

2. _____ The sea creature slept in a dark cave.

3. _____ The old clock ticked quietly on the wall.

4. _____ The baby skunk ran into the woods.

Exercise 2: Use Sentence 4 to underline the complete subject once and the complete predicate twice and to complete the table below.

List the Noun Used	List the Noun Job	Singular or Plural	Common or Proper	Simple Subject	Simple Predicate

Sentence Work

Exercise 3: Underline the **syn** if the words are synonyms. Underline the **ant** if the words are antonyms.

1. first, last   syn ant   3. sleep, doze   syn ant   5. right, wrong   syn ant

2. break, fix   syn ant   4. enemy, friend   syn ant   6. battle, fight   syn ant

Exercise 4: Correct the capitalization mistakes and put the rule number above each correction. Use the rule numbers found in Reference 18 on page 77 in the Reference section of your book.

_____ (Rule numbers)

7. i live at 126 oak street in dallas, texas.   **(Editing Guide: 5 capitalization mistakes)**

_____ (Rule numbers)

8. on monday i will go to dr. chapman.   **(Editing Guide: 5 capitalization mistakes)**

_____ (Rule numbers)

9. my friend lives in oakland, california.   **(Editing Guide: 3 capitalization mistakes)**

UNIT 2: GROUP 10 TEST

Exercise 1: Finding One Part of Speech. For each sentence, write **SN** above the subject and **V** above the verb. Underline the word(s) for the part of speech listed to the left of each sentence.

Adjective(s)   1. A busy squirrel scampered up the tree.

Adverb(s)   2. The birds chirped loudly in the trees.

Noun(s)   3. The goat walked to the car.

Verb(s)   4. An angry man yelled at the dogs.

Preposition(s)   5. The elephants walked slowly through the jungle.

Exercise 2: Use Sentence 5 to complete the table below.

List the Noun Used	List the Noun Job	Singular or Plural	Common or Proper	Simple Subject	Simple Predicate

---

Sentence Work

Exercise 3: Correct the capitalization and punctuation mistakes. Write capitalization rule numbers above and punctuation rule numbers below the corrections. Use References 18 and 19 on page 77 in your Reference section.

_____(Rule numbers)

1. was your sister born on may 31 1990   (Editing Guide: 2 capitals & 2 punctuation)
_____(Rule numbers)

_____(Rule numbers)

2. we will vacation in memphis tennessee   (Editing Guide: 3 capitals & 2 punctuation)
_____(Rule numbers)

_____(Rule numbers)

3. dr thomas b lewis arrives on tuesday   (Editing Guide: 5 capitals & 3 punctuation)
_____(Rule numbers)

UNIT 2: GROUP 11 TEST

Exercise 1: Finding the topic: Write the name of the topic that best describes what each row of words is about. Choose from these topics: Animals, Holidays, Seasons, or Winter Things.

(1)	(2)	(3)
_____	_____	_____
Christmas	snowman	cat
Valentine's Day	coat	dog
Thanksgiving	sled	horse
Independence Day	mittens	bear
Easter	snow shovel	goat

Exercise 2: Words that support the topic: In each row, cross out the one idea that does not support the underlined topic at the top.

(4)	(5)	(6)
Dinner Things	Cleaning Things	Things You Read
fork	mop	magazine
plate	car	book
knife	broom	sheep
bed	dustpan	map
napkin	soap	sign

Exercise 3: Sentences that support the topic: Read the topic. Then, cross out the one sentence that does not support the topic.

Topic: Dressing for Winter

1. Be sure to wear a heavy coat.
2. Building a snowman is fun.
3. Cover your hands with gloves or mittens.
4. Wear a warm hat.

Exercise 4: Sentences that support the topic: Read the topic. Then, cross out the two sentences that do not support the topic.

Topic: Ways Seeds Travel

1. Some seeds fall to the ground.
2. Birds carry seeds and drop them.
3. Some seeds are colorful, and some are plain.
4. Seeds are also carried by the wind.
5. Some seeds stick to moving animals.
6. Small seeds grow into big plants.

UNIT 2: GROUP 12 TEST

Exercise 1: Finding the topic: Write the name of the topic that best describes what each row of words is about. Choose from these topics: Sound Words, Vegetables, Fruits, or Make-Believe.

(1)	(2)	(3)
_____	_____	_____
fairy	moan	apples
dragon	whistle	oranges
ghosts	rumbled	bananas
elf	popped	grapes
goblin	buzzed	plums

Exercise 2: Words that support the topic: In each row, cross out the one idea that does not support the underlined topic at the top.

(4)	(5)	(6)
Vegetables	Meats	Insects
carrots	ham	grasshopper
beans	beef	ant
potatoes	turkey	lizard
apples	chicken	ladybug
peas	pear	butterfly

Exercise 3: Sentences that support the topic: Read the topic. Then, cross out the one sentence that does not support the topic.

Topic: The Equipment of Firemen

1. Firemen spray water on fire from large water hoses.
2. I would like to be a fireman some day.
3. Firemen use different kinds of fire trucks.
4. Firemen wear heavy hats and coats to protect them.

Exercise 4: Sentences that support the topic: Read the topic. Then, cross out the two sentences that do not support the topic.

Topic: Ways to Tell Time

1. Sundials were used to tell time long ago.
2. Watches are made in many different colors.
3. A watch is a common way of telling time.
4. Grandfather clocks are also used to tell time.
5. I want a watch for my birthday.
6. Digital clocks are popular for telling time.

UNIT 3: GROUP 1 TEST

Exercise 1: Classify each sentence. Use **SN** for subject noun, **V** for verb, **Adv** for adverb, **Adj** for adjective, **A** for article adjective, **P** for preposition, **OP** for object of the preposition, and **SP** for subject pronoun.

1. _____We   looked   at   the   funny   bird.

2. _____She   danced   gracefully   around   the   room.

3. _____They   went   to   the   game   today.

4. _____Jim   walked   slowly   to   the   store   yesterday.

Sentence Work

Exercise 2: Underline the <u>syn</u> if the words are synonyms. Underline the <u>ant</u> if the words are antonyms.

1. misplaced, lost	syn ant	3. whisper, shout	syn ant	5. trousers, pants	syn ant
2. add, subtract	syn ant	4. delicious, tasty	syn ant	6. beneath, above	syn ant

---

Exercise 3: Correct the capitalization and punctuation mistakes. Write capitalization rule numbers above and punctuation rule numbers below the corrections. Use References 18 and 19 on page 77 in your Reference section.

_____**(Rule numbers)**

7. dad   went   to   jackson   ohio   **(Editing Guide: 3 capitals & 2 punctuation)**

_____**(Rule numbers)**

_____**(Rule numbers)**

8. is   bill   going   to   newport   florida   **(Editing Guide: 4 capitals & 2 punctuation)**

_____**(Rule numbers)**

_____**(Rule numbers)**

9. mrs   diane   m   scott   left   on   sunday   **(Editing Guide: 5 capitals & 3 punctuation)**

_____**(Rule numbers)**

UNIT 3: GROUP 2 TEST

Exercise 1: Classify each sentence. Use **SP** for subject pronoun and **PP** for possessive pronoun.

1. _____They   came   to   our   house   yesterday.

2. _____The   men   worked   in   our   fields.

3. _____The   spotted   dog   chewed   on   his   bone.

4. _____The   mouse   scampered   quickly   to   his   home.

Sentence Work

Exercise 2: Underline the <u>**syn**</u> if the words are synonyms. Underline the <u>**ant**</u> if the words are antonyms.

1. challenge, dare	syn ant	3. remember, forget	syn ant	5. narrow, wide	syn ant
2. over, under	syn ant	4. possession, belonging	syn ant	6. dark, bright	syn ant

---

Exercise 3: Correct the capitalization and punctuation mistakes. Write capitalization rule numbers above and punctuation rule numbers below the corrections. Use References 18 and 19 on page 77 in your Reference section.

_____(Rule numbers)

7. can   dr   white   see   me   on   july   21   1997   (Editing Guide: 4 capitals & 3 punctuation)

_____Rule numbers)

_____(Rule numbers)

8. we   went   to   the   zoo   on   april   10   1997   (Editing Guide: 2 capitals & 2 punctuation)

_____(Rule numbers)

_____(Rule numbers)

9. mr   jim   w   walker   loves   his   job   (Editing Guide: 4 capitals & 3 punctuation)

_____(Rule numbers)

UNIT 3: GROUP 3 TEST

Exercise 1: Classify each sentence. Use **SP** for subject pronoun, **PP** for possessive pronoun, and **PN** for possessive noun.

1. _____ Mary's sister ran into the brick wall.

2. _____ The brave cat played with my dog's bone.

3. _____ He walked quickly to Tom's house.

4. _____ My brother chewed on my sister's new eraser.

Sentence Work

Exercise 2: Underline the **syn** if the words are synonyms. Underline the **ant** if the words are antonyms.

1. ask, tell	syn ant	3. finished, ended	syn ant	5. independence, freedom	syn ant
2. journey, trip	syn ant	4. inside, outside	syn ant	6. scrumptious, delicious	syn ant

---

Exercise 3: Correct the capitalization and punctuation mistakes. Write capitalization rule numbers above and punctuation rule numbers below the corrections. Use References 18 and 19 on page 77 in your Reference section.

_____(Rule numbers)

7. have you been to grant maryland   (Editing Guide: 3 capitals & 2 punctuation)

_____(Rule numbers)

_____(Rule numbers)

8. dr jackson will be here tuesday   (Editing Guide: 3 capitals & 2 punctuation)

_____(Rule numbers)

_____(Rule numbers)

9. the phone call was for mrs e o adams   (Editing Guide: 5 capitals & 4 punctuation)

_____(Rule numbers)

UNIT 3: GROUP 4 TEST

Exercise 1: Classify each sentence. Use **SP** for subject pronoun, **PP** for possessive pronoun, and **PN** for possessive noun.

1. _____ He jumped quickly into the water.

2. _____ My mother's friend shops during the holidays.

3. _____ Our red car went over hilly roads.

4. _____ My dad's boss arrived early.

Sentence Work

Exercise 2: Underline the <u>syn</u> if the words are synonyms. Underline the <u>ant</u> if the words are antonyms.

1. leap, jump	syn ant	3. leave, depart	syn ant	5. freeze, thaw	syn ant
2. false, true	syn ant	4. braid, weave	syn ant	6. argue, agree	syn ant

---

Exercise 3: Correct the capitalization and punctuation mistakes. Write capitalization rule numbers above and punctuation rule numbers below the corrections. Use References 18 and 19 on page 77 in your Reference section.

_____(Rule numbers)

7. did muffin have kittens in march or april   (Editing Guide: 4 capitals & 1 punctuation)

_____(Rule numbers)

_____(Rule numbers)

8. did mr smith move to oklahoma   (Editing Guide: 4 capitals & 2 punctuation)

_____(Rule numbers)

_____(Rule numbers)

9. will i be late for practice on saturday   (Editing Guide: 3 capitals & 1 punctuation)

_____(Rule numbers)

UNIT 3: GROUP 5 TEST

Exercise 1: Classify each sentence. Use **SP** for subject pronoun, **PP** for possessive pronoun, and **PN** for possessive noun.

1. _____ Beautiful flowers grow in that field.

2. _____ My dog sleeps by my bed.

3. _____ Dad's pencil fell off the table.

Sentence Work

Exercise 2: Underline the <u>syn</u> if the words are synonyms. Underline the <u>ant</u> if the words are antonyms.

1. enjoys, likes	syn ant	3. absent, present	syn ant	5. smile, frown	syn ant
2. friend, buddy	syn ant	4. fawn, deer	syn ant	6. drapes, curtains	syn ant

---

Exercise 3: Correct the capitalization and punctuation mistakes. Write capitalization rule numbers above and punctuation rule numbers below the corrections. Use References 18 and 19 on page 77 in your Reference section.

_____(Rule numbers)

7. mr c s gates fixed my bike   (Editing Guide: 4 capitals & 4 punctuation)

_____(Rule numbers)

_____(Rule numbers)

8. the show starts on june 19 1990   (Editing Guide: 2 capitals & 2 punctuation)

_____(Rule numbers)

_____(Rule numbers)

9. mrs house is my teacher this year   (Editing Guide: 2 capitals & 2 punctuation)

_____(Rule numbers)

UNIT 3: GROUP 6 TEST

Exercise 1: Classify each sentence. Underline the complete subject once and complete predicate twice for Sentence 2.

1. _____ She hurried anxiously to the store.

2. _____ A lovely rainbow appeared over our heads.

3. _____ Her sister's bike fell in the mud.

Exercise 2: Use Sentence 2 to complete the table below.

List the Noun Used	List the Noun Job	Singular or Plural	Common or Proper	Simple Subject	Simple Predicate

Sentence Work

Exercise 3: Underline the **syn** if the words are synonyms. Underline the **ant** if the words are antonyms.

1. alive, dead	syn ant	3. brag, boast	syn ant	5. believe, doubt	syn ant
2. sit, stand	syn ant	4. bold, fearful	syn ant	6. tie, fasten	syn ant

Exercise 4: Correct the capitalization and punctuation mistakes. Write capitalization rule numbers above and punctuation rule numbers below the corrections. Use References 18 and 19 on page 77 in your Reference section.

_____(Rule numbers)

7. jan and i will be back next monday   (Editing Guide: 3 capitals & 1 punctuation)

_____(Rule numbers)

Exercise 5: Write the subject, write **S** for singular or **P** for plural, write the rule number, and underline the correct verb.

Rule 1: A singular subject must use a singular verb form that ends in **s**: *is, was, has, does, or verbs ending with **s** or **es***.
Rule 2: A plural subject or the subject **YOU** must use a plural verb form that has **no s** ending: *are, were, do, have, or verbs without **s** or **es** endings*. (A plural verb form is also called the *plain form*.)

Subject	S or P	Rule

8. The kids (is, are) eating ice cream.
9. A kid (is, are) eating ice cream.
10. A boy (is, are) sitting on the table.
11. Five boys (is, are) sitting on the table.
12. You (is, are) sitting on the table.

UNIT 3: GROUP 7 TEST

Exercise 1: Classify each sentence. Underline the complete subject once and complete predicate twice for Sentence 1.

1. _____ The   swan   glided   softly   across   the   pond.

2. _____ The   customers   waited   impatiently   in   line.

3. _____ My   brother's   friend   crawled   through   the   narrow   tunnel.

Exercise 2: Use Sentence 1 to complete the table below.

List the Noun Used	List the Noun Job	Singular or Plural	Common or Proper	Simple Subject	Simple Predicate

Sentence Work

Exercise 3: Underline the <u>syn</u> if the words are synonyms. Underline the <u>ant</u> if the words are antonyms.

1. beach, shore	syn ant	3. messy, neat	syn ant	5. chuckle, giggle	syn ant
2. mother, father	syn ant	4. cheat, trick	syn ant	6. parent, child	syn ant

Exercise 4: Correct the capitalization and punctuation mistakes. Write capitalization rule numbers above and punctuation rule numbers below the corrections. Use References 18 and 19 on page 77 in your Reference section.

_____(Rule numbers)

7. uncle   jack   was   born   on   june   1   1987   **(Editing Guide: 3 capitals & 2 punctuation)**

_____(Rule numbers)

Exercise 5: Write the subject, write **S** for singular or **P** for plural, write the rule number, and underline the correct verb.

Rule 1: A singular subject must use a singular verb form that ends in **s**: *is, was, has, does, or verbs ending with* **s** *or* **es**.
Rule 2: A plural subject or the subject **YOU** must use a plural verb form that has **no s** ending:
   are, were, do, have, or verbs without **s** *or* **es** *endings.* (A plural verb form is also called the *plain form.*)

Subject	S or P	Rule

8. Nine pumpkins (was, were) growing on the vine.
9. An orange pumpkin (was, were) growing on the vine.
10. A bird (chirps, chirp) outside my window.
11. The birds (chirps, chirp) outside my window.
12. My brother (yells, yell) during the ballgame.
13. You (yells, yell) during the ballgame.

UNIT 3: GROUP 8 TEST

Exercise 1: Finding One Part of Speech. For each sentence, write **SN** or **SP** above the subject and **V** above the verb. Underline the word(s) for the part of speech listed to the left of each sentence.

Adjective(s) 1. The busy ants worked swiftly.   Pronoun(s)   4. I arrived early.

Adverb(s)   2. The music blared loudly today.   Preposition(s) 5. We stood in the shade for hours.

Noun(s)   3. The turtle walked across the road.   Verb(s)   6. A butterfly flew into the room.

Exercise 2: Use Sentence 5 to complete the table below.

List the Noun Used	List the Noun Job	Singular or Plural	Common or Proper	Simple Subject	Simple Predicate

---

Sentence Work

Exercise 3: Underline the <u>syn</u> if the words are synonyms. Underline the <u>ant</u> if the words are antonyms.

1. carpet, rug   syn   ant   3. basement, attic   syn   ant   5. beg, ask   syn   ant
2. friend, pal   syn   ant   4. cheerful, gloomy   syn   ant   6. raise, lower   syn   ant

---

Exercise 4: Correct the capitalization and punctuation mistakes. Write capitalization rule numbers above and punctuation rule numbers below the corrections. Use References 18 and 19 on page 77 in your Reference section.

_____(Rule numbers)

7. dr   fox   will   fix   my   teeth   on   friday   (Editing Guide: 3 capitals & 2 punctuation)

_____(Rule numbers)

Exercise 5: Write the subject, write **S** for singular or **P** for plural, write the rule number, and underline the correct verb.

Rule 1: A singular subject must use a singular verb form that ends in **s**: *is, was, has, does, or verbs ending with **s** or **es**.*
Rule 2: A plural subject or the subject **YOU** must use a plural verb form that has **no s** ending:
    *are, were, do, have, or verbs without **s** or **es** endings.* (A plural verb form is also called the *plain form.*)

Subject	S or P	Rule

8. Mom (shop, shops) for clothes today.

9. Several ladies (shop, shops) for clothes today.

10. That crayon (has, have) melted in the sun.

11. Those crayons (has, have) melted in the sun.

12. Our child (does, do) sing in the play.

13. The pizza (has, have) cheese on it.

14. A few boys (eat, eats) cupcakes for dessert.

15. You (draw, draws) beautiful pictures.

UNIT 3: GROUP 9 TEST

Exercise 1: Match each subject part with the correct predicate part by writing the correct sentence number in the blank.

1. The red car
2. Those big dogs
3. Our school library
4. The children's choir
5. Two raincoats

_____ sang at our program.
_____ has books on snakes.
_____ stopped for a red light.
_____ hung on the coat rack.
_____ barked at the cars.

Exercise 2: Identifying simple sentences and fragments: Write **S** for a complete sentence and **F** for a sentence fragment on the line beside each group of words below.

_____ 6. The birds fly to their nest.
_____ 7. The fire in the fireplace.
_____ 8. I like the circus.
_____ 9. Fell to the ground.
_____ 10. My friend plays with me.
_____ 11. In the water.
_____ 12. Three silly monkeys.
_____ 13. Joe waved at his mom.
_____ 14. This clever trick.
_____ 15. Leaves fall from the trees.

Exercise 3: On your own paper, make each fragment below into a complete sentence. Underline the parts you add.

16. Add a subject part to this fragment: **yelled at the children.**

17. Add a predicate part to this fragment: **The lion in the jungle.**

Exercise 4: Sentences that support the topic: Read the topic. Then, cross out the one sentence that does not support the topic.

Topic: Things Used to Go Camping

1. I have a special tent that I use for camping.
2. I use a sleeping bag to keep me warm at night.
3. I have an apartment that has many windows.
4. I light a lantern after dark to give me light.

Exercise 5: Write the subject, write **S** for singular or **P** for plural, write the rule number, and underline the correct verb.

Rule 1: A singular subject must use a singular verb form that ends in **s**: *is, was, has, does, or verbs ending with **s** or **es**.*
Rule 2: A plural subject or the subject **YOU** must use a plural verb form that has **no s** ending:
*are, were, do, have, or verbs without **s** or **es** endings.* (A plural verb form is also called the *plain form*.)

Subject	S or P	Rule	
			18. Paula (shut, shuts) the door.
			19. Mrs. Jefferson (was, were) reading a book.
			20. Sam (walk, walks) down the street.
			21. The trucks (move, moves) slowly up the steep road.
			22. The bells (is, are) ringing across town.

UNIT 3: GROUP 10 TEST

Exercise 1: Match each subject part with the correct predicate part by writing the correct sentence number in the blank.

1. The angry driver   _____ walks beside his master.
2. The circus parade   _____ leaped quickly across the road.
3. A shy deer   _____ paced back and forth.
4. The angry tiger   _____ shouted at the traffic.
5. A big dog   _____ marches down the street.

Exercise 2: Identifying simple sentences and fragments: Write **S** for a complete sentence and **F** for a sentence fragment on the line beside each group of words below.

_____   6. That red wagon.
_____   7. We walked.
_____   8. To the parade after school.
_____   9. Our family ate supper.
_____   10. The hot, dry desert.
_____   11. The long line moved slowly.
_____   12. A basket of cute kittens.
_____   13. Marty plays football.
_____   14. Running down the hall.
_____   15. We watched the game.

Exercise 3: On your own paper, make each fragment below into a complete sentence. Underline the parts you add.

16. Add a subject part to this fragment: **raced down the road.**

17. Add a predicate part to this fragment: **The driving rain.**

Exercise 4: Sentences that support the topic: Read the topic. Then, cross out the one sentence that does not support the topic.

Topic: Things to Wear

1. I wear shoes and socks during the winter.
2. I listen to my CD player after school.
3. I like wearing jeans to school.
4. I wear my blue shirt for special events.

Exercise 5: Write the subject, write **S** for singular or **P** for plural, write the rule number, and underline the correct verb.

Rule 1: A singular subject must use a singular verb form that ends in **s**: *is, was, has, does, or verbs ending with **s** or **es**.*
Rule 2: A plural subject or the subject **YOU** must use a plural verb form that has **no s** ending: *are, were, do, have, or verbs without **s** or **es** endings.* (A plural verb form is also called the *plain form*.)

Subject	S or P	Rule

18. He (explain, explains) the problem clearly.

19. They (explain, explains) the problem clearly.

20. You (wait, waits) quietly in his office.

21. The walls (was, were) painted today.

22. Mother (is, are) talking to you.

UNIT 4: GROUP 1 TEST

Exercise 1: Classify each sentence. Underline the complete subject once and complete predicate twice for Sentence 1.

1. _____The rocket soared high above the earth.

2. _____Several bees buzzed around my head.

3. _____I dug in my friend's yard for worms.

Exercise 2: Use Sentence 1 to complete the table below.

List the Noun Used	List the Noun Job	Singular or Plural	Common or Proper	Simple Subject	Simple Predicate

Sentence Work

Exercise 3: From Column 1: Write the correct contraction.

1. I am _____

2. is not _____

3. do not _____

4. let us _____

5. we are _____

Exercise 4: From Column 1: Write the correct words.

6. weren't _____

7. that's _____

8. can't _____

9. didn't _____

10. who's _____

Exercise 5: Correct the capitalization and punctuation mistakes. Write capitalization rule numbers above and punctuation rule numbers below the corrections. Use References 18 and 19 on page 77 in your Reference section.

_____**(Rule numbers)**

11. my brother lives on miller road in gil ohio **(Editing Guide: 5 capitals & 2 punctuation)**

_____**(Rule numbers)**

Exercise 6: Write the subject, write **S** for singular or **P** for plural, write the rule number, and underline the correct verb.

Rule 1: A singular subject must use a singular verb form that ends in **s**: *is, was, has, does, or verbs ending with **s** or **es**.*
Rule 2: A plural subject or the subject **YOU** must use a plural verb form that has **no s** ending:
  *are, were, do, have, or verbs without **s** or **es** endings.* (A plural verb form is also called the *plain form.*)

Subject	S or P	Rule

12. The squirrels (gather, gathers) acorns.

13. The squirrel (gather, gathers) acorns.

14. The car (have, has) new tires.

15. Will you (have, has) time to read later?

UNIT 4: GROUP 2 TEST

Exercise 1: Classify each sentence. Underline the complete subject once and complete predicate twice for Sentence 2.

1. _____ He laughed at Billy's joke.

2. _____ I ran after the bus yesterday.

3. _____ My sister's cat leaped over the fence.

Exercise 2: Use Sentence 2 to complete the table below.

List the Noun Used	List the Noun Job	Singular or Plural	Common or Proper	Simple Subject	Simple Predicate

---

Sentence Work

Exercise 3: From Column 2: Write the correct contraction.   **Exercise 4:** From Column 2: Write the correct words.

1. has not _____

2. I will _____

3. will not _____

4. have not _____

5. would not _____

6. I'd _____

7. we'll _____

8. you've _____

9. she's _____

10. shouldn't _____

Exercise 5: Correct the capitalization and punctuation mistakes. Write capitalization rule numbers above and punctuation rule numbers below the corrections. Use References 18 and 19 on page 77 in your Reference section.

_____(Rule numbers)

11. does   rover   obey   your   commands   **(Editing Guide: 2 capitals & 1 punctuation)**

_____(Rule numbers)

Exercise 6: Write the subject, write **S** for singular or **P** for plural, write the rule number, and underline the correct verb.

Rule 1: A singular subject must use a singular verb form that ends in **s**: *is, was, has, does, or verbs ending with* ***s*** *or* ***es***.
Rule 2: A plural subject or the subject **YOU** must use a plural verb form that has **no s** ending: *are, were, do, have, or verbs without* ***s*** *or* ***es*** *endings.* (A plural verb form is also called the *plain form.*)

Subject	S or P	Rule

12. The horses (like, likes) oats.

13. The horse (like, likes) oats.

14. My hotdog (was, were) wrapped in paper.

15. The pizzas (has, have) cheese on them.

16. A red pencil (is, are) in my desk.

17. He (walk, walks) to school.

UNIT 4: GROUP 3 TEST

Exercise 1: Classify each sentence. Underline the complete subject once and complete predicate twice for Sentence 3.

1. _____We ate at my uncle's house today.

2. _____David swims in our pool.

3. _____Sarah went to the lake yesterday.

Exercise 2: Use Sentence 3 to complete the table below.

List the Noun Used	List the Noun Job	Singular or Plural	Common or Proper	Simple Subject	Simple Predicate

---

Sentence Work

Exercise 3: From Column 3: Underline the correct choice.

1. (Its, It's) going to rain.

2. I like (your, you're) hat.

3. (Their, They're) car is new.

4. (Their, They're) leaving at noon.

Exercise 4: From Column 3. Write the correct words.

5. it's _____

6. they're _____

7. who's _____

8. you're _____

Exercise 5: Correct the capitalization and punctuation mistakes. Write capitalization rule numbers above and punctuation rule numbers below the corrections. Use References 18 and 19 on page 77 in your Reference section.

_____(Rule numbers)

9. next monday mr jones travels to albany new york (Editing Guide: **7 capitals & 3 punctuation**)

_____(Rule numbers)

Exercise 6: Write the subject, write **S** for singular or **P** for plural, write the rule number, and underline the correct verb.

Rule 1: A singular subject must use a singular verb form that ends in **s**: *is, was, has, does, or verbs ending with **s** or **es**.*
Rule 2: A plural subject or the subject **YOU** must use a plural verb form that has **no s** ending:
*are, were, do, have, or verbs without **s** or **es** endings.* (A plural verb form is also called the *plain form.*)

Subject	S or P	Rule

10. Only one boy (eat, eats) cupcakes for dessert.

11. A few boys (eat, eats) cupcakes for dessert.

12. The babies (was, were) swimming in the wading pool.

13. You (was, were) swimming in the wading pool.

UNIT 4: GROUP 4 TEST

Exercise 1: Classify each sentence. Underline the complete subject once and complete predicate twice for Sentence 2.

1. _____My   dad   stopped   at   a   small   farm.

2. _____Jim   talked   to   his   pet   bird.

3. _____My   brother   slept   in   Jason's   tent.

Exercise 2: Use Sentence 2 to complete the table below.

List the Noun Used	List the Noun Job	Singular or Plural	Common or Proper	Simple Subject	Simple Predicate

Sentence Work

Exercise 3: From Column 1: Write the correct contraction.

1. what is _____

2. there is _____

3. it is _____

4. was not _____

5. they are _____

Exercise 4: From Column 1: Write the correct words.

6. aren't _____

7. you're _____

8. who's _____

9. she's _____

10. doesn't _____

Exercise 5: Correct the capitalization and punctuation mistakes. Write capitalization rule numbers above and punctuation rule numbers below the corrections. Use References 18 and 19 on page 77 in the Reference section of your book.

_____(Rule numbers)

11. did   mr   j   h   morris   leave   a   message   **(Editing Guide: 5 capitals & 4 punctuation)**

_____(Rule numbers)

Exercise 6: Write the subject, write **S** for singular or **P** for plural, write the rule number, and underline the correct verb.

Rule 1: A singular subject must use a singular verb form that ends in **s**: *is, was, has, does, or verbs ending with* **s** *or* **es**.	
Rule 2: A plural subject or the subject **YOU** must use a plural verb form that has **no s** ending:	
are, were, do, have, or verbs without **s** *or* **es** *endings.* (A plural verb form is also called the *plain form*.)	

Subject	S or P	Rule	
			12. The windows (has, have) curtains.
			13. The baby (was, were) swimming in the pool.
			14. Those new pencils (is, are) in my desk.
			15. Our neighbors (sweep, sweeps) their porch.

UNIT 4: GROUP 5 TEST

Exercise 1: Classify each sentence. Underline the complete subject once and complete predicate twice for Sentence 3.

1. _____A pretty sunflower grows in my neighbor's garden.

2. _____A cute little mouse ran across the floor.

3. _____My brother's ball slammed through the window.

Sentence Work

Exercise 2: Write **a** or **an** in the blanks.

1. Did you get _____ order today?   4. I had _____ steak today.   7. _____ office   10. _____ glove

2. We saw _____ igloo.   5. Dad boiled _____ egg.   8. _____ ball   11. _____ ankle

3. We saw _____ big beaver.   6. Dad boiled _____ potato.   9. _____ acorn   12. _____ dog

Exercise 3: From Column 2: Write the correct contraction.

13. should not _____

14. could not _____

15. he has _____

16. I have _____

17. he will _____

Exercise 4: From Column 2: Write the correct words.

18. she'll _____

19. you'd _____

20. hasn't _____

21. they've _____

22. I'd _____

Exercise 5: Correct the capitalization and punctuation mistakes. Write capitalization rule numbers above and punctuation rule numbers below the corrections. Use References 18 and 19 on page 77 in the Reference section of your book.

_____(Rule numbers)

23. does ann live at 725 circle drive in columbus ohio   **(Editing Guide: 6 capitals & 2 punctuation)**

_____(Rule numbers)

Exercise 6: Write the subject, write **S** for singular or **P** for plural, write the rule number, and underline the correct verb.

Rule 1: A singular subject must use a singular verb form that ends in **s**: *is, was, has, does, or verbs ending with* **s** *or* **es**.
Rule 2: A plural subject or the subject **YOU** must use a plural verb form that has **no s** ending: *are, were, do, have, or verbs without* **s** *or* **es** *endings.* (A plural verb form is also called the *plain form.*)

Subject	S or P	Rule

24. Susan's pictures (has, have) lots of colors.

25. The dish (was, were) in the sink.

26. Our friends (was, were) playing football.

27. We (talk, talks) to students about our trip.

UNIT 4: GROUP 6 TEST

Exercise 1: Classify each sentence. Underline the complete subject once and complete predicate twice for Sentence 3.

1. _____The friendly dog jumped on my new dress.

2. _____The cold campers sat by the warm fire.

3. _____A shy brown deer peeked from the dark woods.

Sentence Work

Exercise 2: Write **a** or **an** in the blanks.

1. We saw _____ lion today.   4. It is _____ clever pony.   7. ____ elbow   10. ____ mop

2. It was _____ amazing lion.   5. It was _____ easy test.   8. ____ lamp   11. ____ ax

3. We have _____ unusual pet.   6. We want _____ ride.   9. ____ opinion   12. ____ box

Exercise 3: From Column 3: Underline the correct choice.

13. The deer went (its, it's) own way.

14. Our family wants (your, you're) advice.

15. Today (their, they're) very happy.

16. We like (their, they're) new house.

Exercise 4: From Column 3. Write the correct words.

17. who's _____

18. you're _____

19. it's _____

20. they're _____

Exercise 5: Correct the capitalization and punctuation mistakes. Write capitalization rule numbers above and punctuation rule numbers below the corrections. Use References 18 and 19 on page 77 in the Reference section of your book.

_____(Rule numbers)

21. jane and i wrote to mrs blue in denver colorado (**Editing Guide: 6 capitals & 3 punctuation**)

_____(Rule numbers)

Exercise 6: Write the subject, write **S** for singular or **P** for plural, write the rule number, and underline the correct verb.

Rule 1: A singular subject must use a singular verb form that ends in **s**: *is, was, has, does, or verbs ending with **s** or **es**.*
Rule 2: A plural subject or the subject **YOU** must use a plural verb form that has **no s** ending:
   *are, were, do, have, or verbs without **s** or **es** endings.* (A plural verb form is also called the *plain form*.)

Subject	S or P	Rule

22. The games (is, are) today.

23. The snake (crawl, crawls) through the grass.

24. The boys (has, have) a new boat.

25. He (don't, doesn't) like carrots.

UNIT 4: GROUP 7 TEST

Exercise 1: Classify each sentence. Underline the complete subject once and complete predicate twice for Sentence 1.

1. _____The   white   owls   sat   in   the   tall   trees.

2. _____The   excited   dogs   barked   at   the   little   rabbit.

3. _____The   noisy   boys   played   outside.

Sentence Work

Exercise 2: Write **a** or **an** in the blanks.

1. We rode _____ elephant.	4. Did you see _____ owl?	7. ____ fan 10. ____ olive
2. He was _____ funny clown.	5. I have _____ guitar.	8. ____ friend 11. ____ egg
3. We ate _____ salad.	6. I need _____ umbrella.	9. ____ Indian 12. ____ car

Exercise 3: From Column 1: Write the correct contraction.

13. I am _____

14. there is _____

15. are not _____

16. were not _____

17. did not _____

Exercise 4: From Column 1: Write the correct words.

18. can't _____

19. wasn't _____

20. isn't _____

21. we're _____

22. you're _____

Exercise 5: Correct the capitalization and punctuation mistakes. Write capitalization rule numbers above and punctuation rule numbers below the corrections. Use References 18 and 19 on page 77 in the Reference section of your book.

_____(Rule numbers)

23. may i call you back next wednesday   (Editing Guide: 3 capitals & 1 punctuation)

_____(Rule numbers)

Exercise 6: Write the subject, write **S** for singular or **P** for plural, write the rule number, and underline the correct verb.

Rule 1: A singular subject must use a singular verb form that ends in **s**: *is, was, has, does, or verbs ending with **s** or **es**.*
Rule 2: A plural subject or the subject **YOU** must use a plural verb form that has **no s** ending:
*are, were, do, have, or verbs without **s** or **es** endings.* (A plural verb form is also called the *plain form*.)

Subject	S or P	Rule

24. You (is, are) my best friend.

25. Mary (dive, dives) from the high board.

26. They (race, races) in the pool.

27. We (has, have) a new bike.

UNIT 4: GROUP 8 TEST

Exercise 1: Match each subject part with the correct predicate part by writing the correct sentence number in the blank.

1. The student   _____ scampered up the tree.
2. The early settlers   _____ recited the poem.
3. The tiny squirrel   _____ sails at noon.
4. The ship   _____ raised corn.
5. The old building   _____ needs painting.

Exercise 2: Identifying simple sentences and fragments: Write **S** for a complete sentence and **F** for a sentence fragment on the line beside each group of words below.

_____ 6. He has a new coat.
_____ 7. Hurt her finger at work.
_____ 8. Fred's mother.
_____ 9. John found a dime.
_____ 10. Has a funny hat.
_____ 11. Bill played baseball.
_____ 12. Wore her new dress to the party.
_____ 13. LaShona loves the pretty flowers.
_____ 14. The tired little baby.
_____ 15. In the cool pond.

Exercise 3: On your own paper, make each fragment below into a complete sentence. Underline the parts you add.

16. Add a subject part to this fragment: **screamed loudly.**

17. Add a predicate part to this fragment: **All the students.**

Exercise 4: Sentences that support the topic: Read the topic. Then, cross out the one sentence that does not support the topic.

Topic: Things to Take to Camp

1. Cindy packed paper and envelopes for writing home.
2. She put soap, shampoo, and a toothbrush in a plastic bag.
3. Cindy also took play clothes and a bathing suit.
4. Cindy went to the movies with her friends.

Exercise 5: Write the subject, write **S** for singular or **P** for plural, write the rule number, and underline the correct verb.

Rule 1: A singular subject must use a singular verb form that ends in **s**: *is, was, has, does, or verbs ending with **s** or **es***. Rule 2: A plural subject or the subject **YOU** must use a plural verb form that has **no s** ending: *are, were, do, have, or verbs without **s** or **es** endings*. (A plural verb form is also called the *plain form*.)

Subject	S or P	Rule	
			18. Ann's horses (was, were) eating hay.
			19. The sailor (is, are) going to sea.
			20. Those flies (was, were) bothering us.
			21. Maria's pet bird (talk, talks) to everyone.
			22. His dogs (travel, travels) to dog shows.

Level 2 Student Workbook

UNIT 4: GROUP 9 TEST

Exercise 1: Match each subject part with the correct predicate part by writing the correct sentence number in the blank.

1. That math student   _____ sewed a button on my shirt.
2. My mother   _____ needs to be sharpened.
3. The large book   _____ broke down yesterday.
4. My pencil   _____ has lots of pictures.
5. The school bus   _____ studied hard for his test.

Exercise 2: Identifying simple sentences and fragments: Write **S** for a complete sentence and **F** for a sentence fragment on the line beside each group of words below.

_____   6. Talks on the phone.
_____   7. Hungry wolves circled the deer.
_____   8. By the campfire.
_____   9. Three trucks dumped dirt on the road.
_____ 10. The train whistle blew.
_____ 11. The cars raced around the track.
_____ 12. After the game.
_____ 13. We cheered loudly.
_____ 14. The wolves howled.
_____ 15. The lovely flowers.

Exercise 3: On your own paper, make each fragment below into a complete sentence. Underline the parts you add.

16. Add a subject part to this fragment: **climbed down the steep mountain.**
17. Add a predicate part to this fragment: **The burglar.**

Exercise 4: Sentences that support the topic: Read the topic. Then, cross out the one sentence that does not support the topic.

Topic: Different Kinds of Dance

1. My dance teacher teaches different kinds of dance.
2. She has a ballet class in the afternoons.
3. She doesn't like stormy weather.
4. Her tap and jazz classes are on Saturday.

Exercise 5: Write the subject, write **S** for singular or **P** for plural, write the rule number, and underline the correct verb.

Subject	S or P	Rule	
Rule 1: A singular subject must use a singular verb form that ends in **s**: *is, was, has, does, or verbs ending with **s** or **es**.*			
Rule 2: A plural subject or the subject **YOU** must use a plural verb form that has **no s** ending: *are, were, do, have, or verbs without **s** or **es** endings.* (A plural verb form is also called the *plain form.*)			

Subject	S or P	Rule	
			18. Mrs. Brown (own, owns) a pet store.
			19. Two gerbils (stare, stares) at us.
			20. Greg's friends (has, have) bikes to ride.
			21. The games (was, were) fun.
			22. My sisters (do, does) the dishes.

UNIT 5: GROUP 1 TEST

Exercise 1: Classify each sentence. Underline the complete subject once and complete predicate twice for Sentence 2.

1. _____ My   mother   sits   under   a   large   umbrella.

2. _____ Eight   brown   bears   danced   around   the   ring.

3. _____ Seven   lions   jumped   through   a   round   hoop.

Sentence Work

Exercise 2: Identify the tense of each underlined verb tense by writing a number **1** for present tense, a number **2** for past tense, or a number **3** for future tense. Use the verb chant chart for the irregular verbs.

Verb Tense	Regular Verbs	Verb Tense	Irregular Verbs
	1. School <u>will close</u> for the summer.		5. Wendy <u>wore</u> a red dress.
	2. School <u>closed</u> for the summer.		6. Wendy <u>wears</u> a red dress.
	3. School <u>closes</u> for the summer.		7. Wendy <u>will wear</u> a red dress.
	4. We <u>watch</u> the movie together.		8. He <u>wrote</u> a beautiful poem.

Exercise 3: Write **a** or **an** in the blanks.

9. Do you want _____ orange?   11. I need _____ new coat.   13. _____ marble   15. _____ angel

10. I will buy _____ ink pen.   12. I saw _____ deer.   14. _____ actor   16. _____ card

Exercise 4: From Column 1: Write the correct contraction.

17. I am   _____

18. he is   _____

19. cannot   _____

20. are not   _____

21. was not   _____

Exercise 5: From Column 1: Write the correct words.

22. isn't   _____

23. you're   _____

24. weren't   _____

25. didn't   _____

26. don't   _____

Exercise 6: Write the subject, write **S** for singular or **P** for plural, write the rule number, and underline the correct verb.

Rule 1: A singular subject must use a singular verb form that ends in **s**: *is, was, has, does, or verbs ending with* **s** *or* **es**.
Rule 2: A plural subject or the subject **YOU** must use a plural verb form that has **no s** ending: *are, were, do, have, or verbs without* **s** *or* **es** *endings.* (A plural verb form is also called the *plain form.*)

Subject	S or P	Rule	
			27. The elephants (has, have) long trunks.
			28. Those babies (cry, cries) a lot.
			29. The wind (is, are) blowing hard.
			30. My boat (race, races) tomorrow.

UNIT 5: GROUP 2 TEST

Exercise 1: Classify each sentence. Underline the complete subject once and complete predicate twice for Sentence 1.

1. _____ Several   fleas   hopped   on   my   dog.

2. _____ My   horse   galloped   eagerly   around   the   track.

3. _____ Seven   apples   fell   to   the   ground.

Sentence Work

Exercise 2: Identify the tense of each underlined verb tense by writing a number **1** for present tense, a number **2** for past tense, or a number **3** for future tense. Use the verb chant chart for the irregular verbs.

Verb Tense	Regular Verbs	Verb Tense	Irregular Verbs
	1. The boats <u>sailed</u> on the ocean.		5. We <u>will drive</u> to town.
	2. The children <u>wave</u> to the ranger.		6. His grass <u>grows</u> fast.
	3. We <u>will circle</u> the lake.		7. They <u>went</u> on vacation.
	4. Our puppy <u>rolled</u> in the mud.		8. Mom <u>bought</u> groceries.

Exercise 3: Write **a** or **an** in the blanks.

9. I have _____ eye appointment.   11. We built _____ fire.   13. _____ visitor   15. _____ jar

10. He attended _____ meeting.   12. He is _____ old man.   14. _____ airplane   16. _____ pet

Exercise 4: From Column 2: Write the correct contraction.

17. has not _____

18. have not _____

19. I have _____

20. will not _____

21. would not _____

Exercise 5: From Column 2: Write the correct words.

22. couldn't _____

23. you'll _____

24. I'd _____

25. we've _____

26. he's _____

Exercise 6: Write the subject, write **S** for singular or **P** for plural, write the rule number, and underline the correct verb.

Rule 1: A singular subject must use a singular verb form that ends in **s**: *is, was, has, does, or verbs ending with **s** or **es***.
Rule 2: A plural subject or the subject **YOU** must use a plural verb form that has **no s** ending:
    *are, were, do, have, or verbs without **s** or **es** endings.* (A plural verb form is also called the *plain form*.)

Subject	S or P	Rule	
			27. Latoya (run, runs) on the track team.
			28. My puppy (dig, digs) up our flowers.
			29. The wild birds (has, have) strong wings.
			30. The girls (is, are) going shopping.

UNIT 5: GROUP 3 TEST

Exercise 1: Classify each sentence. Underline the complete subject once and complete predicate twice for Sentence 2.

1. _____My   cold   kitten   ran   into   our   warm   house.

2. _____Joe's   dog   growled   at   the   mailman.

3. _____The   beaver   family   swam   around   the   pond.

Sentence Work

Exercise 2: Identify the tense of each underlined verb tense by writing a number **1** for present tense, a number **2** for past tense, or a number **3** for future tense. Use the verb chant chart for the irregular verbs.

Verb Tense	Regular Verbs	Verb Tense	Irregular Verbs
	1. He <u>planted</u> a tree.		5. Mike <u>chose</u> a hotdog for lunch.
	2. They <u>will visit</u> their family.		6. They <u>sell</u> school supplies.
	3. Carlos <u>lives</u> with his grandmother.		7. We <u>will swim</u> tomorrow.
	4. The children <u>played</u> tag in the yard.		8. He <u>begins</u> his work early.

Exercise 3: Write **a** or **an** in the blanks.

9. I would like _____ radish.   11. We bought _____ kite.   13. _____ elf   15. _____ barn

10. I want _____ alarm clock.   12. He shot _____ arrow.   14. _____ list   16. _____ ant

Exercise 4: From Column 3: Underline the correct choice.

17. (Its, It's) going to rain.

18. I like (your, you're) hat.

19. (Their, They're) car is new.

20. (Their, They're) leaving at noon.

Exercise 5: From Column 3. Write the correct words.

21.   it's   _____

22.   they're   _____

23.   who's   _____

24.   you're   _____

Exercise 6: Correct the capitalization and punctuation mistakes Write capitalization rule numbers above and punctuation rule numbers below the corrections. Use References 18 and 19 on page 77 in the Reference section of your book.

_____**(Rule numbers)**

1. linda and i gave prince a bath on monday   **(Editing Guide: 4 capitals & 1 punctuation)**

_____**(Rule numbers)**

UNIT 5: GROUP 4 TEST

Exercise 1: Classify each sentence. Underline the complete subject once and complete predicate twice for Sentence 3.

1. _____ Two   rivers   flooded   during   the   storm.

2. _____ Jennifer's   mom   stepped   in   the   mud.

3. _____ My   puppy's   bone   landed   in   Dad's   plate.

Sentence Work

Exercise 2: Identify the tense of each underlined verb tense by writing a number **1** for present tense, a number **2** for past tense, or a number **3** for future tense. Use the verb chant chart for the irregular verbs.

Verb Tense	Regular Verbs	Verb Tense	Irregular Verbs
	1. I <u>spilled</u> my milk.		7. My sister <u>sings</u> in the choir.
	2. Maria <u>carries</u> her lunch.		8. I <u>drank</u> my glass of milk.
	3. My father <u>owns</u> a red tractor.		9. We <u>went</u> hiking in the mountains.
	4. The farmer <u>will plant</u> corn.		10. They <u>will freeze</u> ice cream.
	5. The kitten <u>plays</u> with a ball of yarn.		11. We <u>see</u> the sunrise.
	6. They <u>will fix</u> sandwiches for lunch.		12. He <u>came</u> home.

Exercise 3: Write **a** or **an** in the blanks.

13. I want _____ ham salad.   15. We bought _____ oil lamp.   17. ____ otter   19. ____ car

14. He turned down _____ alley.   16. I watched _____ movie.   18. ____ star   20. ____ arm

Exercise 4: From Column 1: Write the correct contraction.

21. are not _____

22. who is _____

23. cannot _____

24. you are _____

Exercise 5: From Column 1: Write the correct words.

25. didn't _____

26. don't _____

27. we're _____

28. there's _____

Exercise 6: Underline the correct homonym in each sentence.

29. My dad jogs (to, too, two) miles every day.

30. Would you like to go (to, too, two)?

31. We will go (to, too, two) the park.

32. (Its, It's) a beautiful day!

33. My shoes are (knew, new).

34. (There, Their, They're) working tonight.

35. Do you want (your, you're) candy?

36. I will (write, right) Grandma a letter.

37. I want to (buy, by) a CD.

38. Did you (hear, here) the radio report?

UNIT 5: GROUP 5 TEST

Exercise 1: Classify each sentence. Underline the complete subject once and complete predicate twice for Sentence 1.

1. _____The   gentle   dragon   returned   sadly   to   the   forest.

2. _____The   two   eagles   soared   over   the   mountaintop.

3. _____He   smiled   at   Emily's   funny   face.

Sentence Work	

Exercise 2: Identify the tense of each underlined verb tense by writing a number **1** for present tense, a number **2** for past tense, or a number **3** for future tense. Use the verb chant chart for the irregular verbs.

Verb Tense	Regular Verbs	Verb Tense	Irregular Verbs
	1. Joey <u>pulls</u> the wagon home.		7. My brother <u>broke</u> a dish.
	2. The frog <u>jumped</u> in the pond.		8. My grandmother <u>comes</u> often.
	3. The boys <u>play</u> on the slide.		9. The pitcher <u>throws</u> the ball.
	4. The girls <u>played</u> on the swings.		10. They <u>will sit</u> on the floor.
	5. Dad <u>helps</u> me every night.		11. The bell <u>rings</u> for recess.
	6. The bear <u>will sleep</u> all winter.		12. The visitors <u>went</u> on a tour.

Exercise 3: Write **a** or **an** in the blanks.

13. It is _____ cold day. 15. He had _____ ear infection. 17. _____ order 19. _____ bus

14. I had _____ overdue book. 16. They had _____ iron gate. 18. _____ oven 20. _____ outfit

Exercise 4: From Column 2: Write the correct contraction.

21. has not   _____

22. have not   _____

23. could not   _____

24. I will   _____

Exercise 5: From Column 1: Write the correct words.

25. she's   _____

26. you've   _____

27. they'll   _____

28. you'd   _____

Exercise 6: Underline the correct homonym in each sentence.

29. I love the (peace, piece) of country living.

30. My ankles are very (week, weak).

31. They like (our, hour) new game.

32. I want a (peace, piece) of pie.

33. We (knew, new) the answers.

34. (There, Their, They're) team won!

35. (Your, You're) a good swimmer.

36. We go to camp for a (weak, week).

37. I know this answer is not (write, right).

38. (Hear, Here) are my keys!

UNIT 5: GROUP 6 TEST

Exercise 1: Classify each sentence. Underline the complete subject once and complete predicate twice for Sentence 3.

1. _____ The balloon man waved to the children.

2. _____ My sister's friend looked for pretty shells.

3. _____ The old tractor rusted in the barn.

Sentence Work

Exercise 2: Identify the tense of each underlined verb tense by writing a number **1** for present tense, a number **2** for past tense, or a number **3** for future tense. Use the verb chant chart for the irregular verbs.

Verb Tense	Regular Verbs	Verb Tense	Irregular Verbs
	1. Those bears <u>look</u> hungry.		7. The students <u>began</u> their tests.
	2. We <u>worked</u> at the library.		8. The cows <u>give</u> lots of milk.
	3. I <u>will call</u> my friend tonight.		9. Our company <u>makes</u> candy.
	4. Mom <u>studied</u> after dinner.		10. They <u>will swim</u> tomorrow.
	5. We <u>will help</u> you with the dishes.		11. I <u>did</u> a few chores.
	6. My friends <u>stayed</u> for lunch.		12. He <u>ran</u> in the big race.

Exercise 3: Write **a** or **an** in the blanks.

13. Sherry carries _____ case.   15. I played _____ old song.   17. _____ adult   19. ____ cake

14. I take _____ exercise class.   16. Sam saw _____ open door.   18. _____ calf   20. _____ idea

Exercise 4: From Column 3: Underline the correct choice.

21. (Whose, Who's) playing the drums?

22. There is (your, you're) Mom.

23. The deer hides (its, it's) baby.

24. (Their, They're) soccer team is a winner.

Exercise 5: From Column 3. Write the correct words.

25. you're _____

26. they're _____

27. who's _____

28. it's _____

Exercise 6: Underline the correct homonym in each sentence.

29. We stopped (buy, by) the store.

30. I want to stop (hear, here) for lunch.

31. I like this game (to, too, two).

32. Here is (your, you're) change.

33. The food is over (their, there, they're).

34. I have a (weak, week) to do this homework.

35. We want (peace, piece) for our country.

36. It will take us an (our, hour) to finish.

37. I like the (knew, new) rules.

38. There is a table (buy, by) the bed.

UNIT 5: GROUP 7 TEST

Exercise 1: Classify each sentence. Underline the complete subject once and complete predicate twice for Sentence 3.

1. _____ The family played at the park.

2. _____ The old car bumped along the highway.

3. _____ The big fish flopped noisily into the water.

Sentence Work

Exercise 2: Identify the tense of each underlined verb tense by writing a number **1** for present tense, a number **2** for past tense, or a number **3** for future tense. Use the verb chant chart for the irregular verbs.

Verb Tense	Regular Verbs	Verb Tense	Irregular Verbs
	1. Jalene <u>ordered</u> seeds last week.		5. The storm <u>begins</u> in an hour.
	2. Dad <u>will pull</u> the sled for Tim.		6. Mr. Lee <u>buys</u> a newspaper.
	3. The children <u>work</u> very hard.		7. We <u>ate</u> an early breakfast.
	4. The workers <u>plowed</u> the roads.		8. We <u>will drink</u> juice with our meal.

Exercise 3: Correct the capitalization and punctuation mistakes. Write capitalization rule numbers above and punctuation rule numbers below the corrections. Use References 18 and 19 on page 77 in the Reference section of your book.

_____ (Rule numbers)

9. has mrs tanner arrived in memphis tennessee   (Editing Guide: 5 capitals & 3 punctuation)

_____ (Rule numbers)

Exercise 4: From Column 1: Write the correct contraction.

10. I am _____

11. is not _____

12. are not _____

13. do not _____

Exercise 5: From Column 1: Write the correct words.

14. can't _____

15. didn't _____

16. you're _____

17. it's _____

Exercise 6: Underline the correct homonym in each sentence.

18. I want to (hear, here) the speaker.

19. (Its, It's) an important meeting.

20. I (knew, new) where Janet lived.

21. (Our, Hour) car is in the garage.

22. There is a (peace, piece) of broken glass.

23. He bought (to, too, two) chickens.

POSTTEST—PATTERN 1

Exercise 1: Tell how each word is used in the sentences by writing the part of speech above the word. (Use the abbreviations learned in the Shurley Method.)

1. _____The   frightened   little   rabbit   ran   away   quickly.

2. _____My   father's   big   clock   ticked   loudly   on   the   wall.

3. _____I   laughed   at   my   dad's   funny   clown   suit.

4. What are the Adjective Questions? _____

5. What are the Adverb Questions? _____

Exercise 2: Put capital letters and marks of punctuation as needed in the sentences below.

6. last   week   joe   went   to   dallas   texas

7. i   want   sam   to   help   me   find   mr   williams

8. did   aunt   ruth   say   that   uncle   tom   was   born   on   may   20   1965

Exercise 3: Write **S** for a complete sentence or **F** for a sentence fragment on the line beside each group of words.

_____ 9. The boats sailed around the lake.   _____ 11. The angry panther in the jungle.

_____ 10. Blew out of the mountains for an hour.   _____ 12. We walked to school.

Exercise 4: Write S for singular or P for plural.	
Noun	**S or P**
13. gloves	
14. blanket	
15. plates	

Exercise 5: Write C for common or P for proper.	
Noun	**C or P**
16. Oklahoma	
17. turkey	
18. Mr. West	

Exercise 6: Underline the complete subject once and the complete predicate twice.

19. The five beavers worked quickly.   20. The big elephants walked through the jungle.

Exercise 7: Underline the simple subject once and the simple predicate twice.

21. The geese flew for hours.   22. The little kittens played with the yarn.

Exercise 8: On the back of this posttest, write a paragraph on this topic: "What I Think About English."

What I Think About English

UNIT 6: GROUP 1A TEST

Exercise 1: Write the parts of a friendly letter in the correct places in the friendly letter below.

1. **Heading**   2. **Greeting**   3. **Closing**   4. **Signature**

   45 Oak Drive   Dear Grandma,   Your grandson,   Tommy
   Lynn, Utah 03020
   July 2, 20___

5. **Body**

   My cat had kittens today. I am saving two kittens just for you. They will be ready in six weeks.

Friendly Letter

Heading _____

_____

_____

_____

Greeting _____

_____

Body _____

_____

_____

_____

Closing _____

_____

Signature _____

_____

UNIT 6: GROUP 3 TEST

Exercise 1: Unscramble the parts of the friendly letter. Write the title parts and the sample parts in the correct blanks on the letter and envelope below. Draw a stamp in the proper place on the envelope.

Title Parts of a Friendly Letter

1. Closing   3. Signature   5. Heading

2. Greeting   4. Body

Sample Parts of a Friendly Letter

1. March 5, 20___   4. 12 Queen Street   6. Sandy

2. Dear Ann,   5. Your aunt,   7. Adams, Maine 63421

3. Your mom told me that you won an art award. I am so proud of you. Keep working hard!

Friendly Letter

1. Title: _____

Example: _____

_____

_____

2. Title: _____

Example: _____

3. Title: _____

Example: _____

_____

_____

4. Title: _____

Example: _____

5. Title: _____

Example: _____

Title Parts of an Envelope:

1. Return Address

2. Mailing Address

Sample Parts of an Envelope:

1. Sandy Allen (writer)

   12 Queen Street

   Adams, Maine 63421

2. Ann Jackson (receiver)

   40 Linda Lane

   Orlando, Florida 93678

6. Title

_____

_____

7. Title

_____

_____

_____

UNIT 6: GROUP 4 TEST

Exercise 1: Unscramble the parts of the friendly letter. Write the title parts and the sample parts in the correct blanks on the letter and envelope below. Draw a stamp in the proper place on the envelope.

Title Parts of a Friendly Letter
1. Closing
2. Greeting
3. Signature
4. Body
5. Heading

Sample Parts of a Friendly Letter
1. June 15, 20___
2. Dear Grandma,
3. We saw your picture in the newspaper for winning the contest. Your quilt is pretty. What did you win?
4. 2 Valley Drive
5. Love,
6. Cindy
7. Crane, Texas 70021

Friendly Letter

1. Title: _____
Example:
_____
_____
_____

2. Title: _____
Example:
_____

3. Title: _____
Example:
_____
_____
_____

4. Title: _____
Example:
_____

5. Title: _____
Example:
_____

Title Parts of an Envelope:
1. Return Address
2. Mailing Address

Sample Parts of an Envelope:
1. Cindy Adams (writer)
2 Valley Drive
Crane, Texas 70021

2. Helen Thomas (receiver)
13 Oak Street
Kent, Texas 71405

6. Title: _____

7. Title: _____

UNIT 6: GROUP 5 TEST

Exercise 1: Using the information given below, you are to write a friendly letter on your own notebook paper, and you are to address the envelope on this page. Draw a stamp in the proper place on the envelope.

Information for your letter and envelope

Your name is _____**(student's name)**_____ .

Your address is 22 Rock Road, Cabot, Georgia 33415.

You have just moved to a new town. You are writing your friend in your old town a letter to tell him/her about your new school. Be sure to tell him/her about your teacher and your new friends.

Your friend's name is ___**(you fill in the first name)**___ York. He / she lives in your old town, at 31 Smart Street, Troy, Ohio 35098.

Level 2 Student Workbook

© SHURLEY INSTRUCTIONAL MATERIALS, INC.

UNIT 7: GROUP 1 TEST

Exercise 1: Write the letters in each group below in alphabetical order.

1. n b h a _____

2. a q l s _____

3. r c m f a p _____

4. c b z h r o _____

5. g l b t m u f o _____

6. t w a c m p e s _____

Exercise 2: Put each group of words in alphabetical order. Use numbers to show the order in each column.

Animal Words	**Food Words**	**"C" Words**
_____ 7. ant	_____ 9. eggs	_____ 11. cat
_____ 8. zebra	_____ 10. bacon	_____ 12. cow

Exercise 3: Put each group of words in alphabetical order. Use numbers to show the order in each column.

House Words	**School Words**	**"M" Words**
_____ 13. den	_____ 16. teacher	_____ 19. man
_____ 14. kitchen	_____ 17. class	_____ 20. Monday
_____ 15. bedroom	_____ 18. library	

Exercise 4: Put each group of words in alphabetical order. Use numbers to show the order in each column.

Space Words	**Toy Words**	**"T" Words**
_____ 21. planet	_____ 25. doll	_____ 29. truck
_____ 22. sun	_____ 26. ball	_____ 30. tan
_____ 23. moon	_____ 27. games	
_____ 24. Earth	_____ 28. kite	

UNIT 7: GROUP 2 TEST

Exercise 1: Label each part of the dictionary entry below. Use Reference 43 on page 90 to help you.

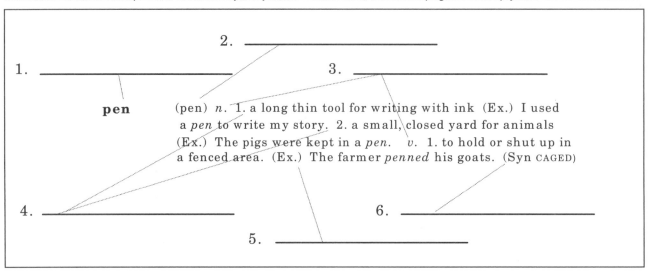

2. _____

1. _____   3. _____

pen   (pen) *n.* 1. a long thin tool for writing with ink (Ex.) I used
a *pen* to write my story. 2. a small, closed yard for animals
(Ex.) The pigs were kept in a *pen.*   *v.* 1. to hold or shut up in
a fenced area. (Ex.) The farmer *penned* his goats. (Syn CAGED)

4. _____   6. _____

5. _____

Exercise 2: Use Reference 43 to match the definitions. Write the correct letter of the word beside each definition.

_____ 7. how to pronounce a word, usually put in parentheses   A.   pronunciation

_____ 8. correct spelling and divides the word into syllables   B.   meanings

_____ 9. numbered definitions listed according to the part of speech   C.   entry word

_____ 10. a small *n.* for noun, a small *v.* for verb, an *adj.* for adjective, etc.   D.   synonyms

_____ 11. a sentence using the entry word to explain a meaning   E.   parts of speech

_____ 12. words that have similar meanings to the entry word   F.   example

Exercise 3: Match each underlined word with its correct meaning. Write the letter in the blank.

_____ 13. Grandma gave me a red ink <u>pen</u>.   A.   *v.* to hold or shut up in a fenced area

_____ 14. Don will <u>pen</u> his horses in a corral.   B.   *n.* a small, closed yard for animals

_____ 15. Diane put the puppies in a <u>pen</u> outside.   C.   *n.* a long thin tool for writing with ink

Exercise 4: Put each group of words in alphabetical order. Use numbers to show the order in each column.

Time Words	Tree Words	Day Words
_____ 16. hour	_____ 18. oak	_____ 20. Tuesday
_____ 17. minute	_____ 19. pine	_____ 21. Monday

UNIT 7: GROUP 3 TEST

Exercise 1: Match each part of a book listed below with the type of information it may give you. Write the appropriate letter in the blank. You may use a letter only once. Use Reference 44 on page 91 in your Reference section.

A. Title page	B. Table of contents	C. Copyright page	D. Index	E. Bibliography
F. Body	G. Glossary			

1. _____ Meanings of important words in the book

2. _____ Exact page numbers for a particular topic

3. _____ Copyright date

4. _____ Books listed for finding more information

5. _____ Text of the book

6. _____ Titles of units and chapters

7. _____ Author's name, title of book, and illustrator's name

Exercise 2: Name the four parts found at the front of a book.

8. _____

9. _____

10. _____

11. _____

Exercise 3: Name the three parts found at the back of a book.

12. _____

13. _____

14. _____

Student's Notes

LEVEL 2

JINGLE

SECTION

Jingle Section

Jingle 1: Sentence Jingle

A sentence, sentence, sentence
Is complete, complete, complete
When 5 simple rules
It meets, meets, meets.

It has a subject, subject, subject
And a verb, verb, verb.
It makes sense, sense, sense
With every word, word, word.

Add a capital letter, letter,
And an end mark, mark.
Now, we're finished, and aren't we smart!
Now, our sentence has all its parts!

REMEMBER
Subject, Verb, Com-plete sense,
Capital letter, and an end mark, too.
That's what a sentence is all about!

Jingle 2: Noun Jingle

This little noun,
Floating around,
Names a person, place, or thing.
With a knick knack, paddy wack,
These are English rules.
Isn't language fun and cool?

Jingle 3: Verb Jingle

A verb shows action,
There's no doubt!
It tells what the subject does,
Like sing and shout.

Action verbs are fun to do.
Now, it's time to name a few.
So, clap your hands and join our rhyme;
Say those verbs in record time!

Wiggle, jiggle, turn around,
Raise your arms and stomp the ground.
Shake your finger and wink your eye;
Wave those action verbs good-bye.

Jingle Section

Jingle 4: Adverb Jingle

An adverb modifies a verb, adjective, or another adverb.
An adverb asks *How? When? Where?*
To find an adverb: **Go, Ask, Get**.
Where do I **go**? To a verb, adjective, or another adverb.
What do I **ask**? How? When? Where?
What do I **get**? An ADVERB! (Clap) That's what!

Jingle 5: Adjective Jingle

An adjective modifies a noun or pronoun.
An adjective asks *What kind? Which one? How many?*
To find an adjective: **Go, Ask, Get**.
Where do I **go**? To a noun or pronoun.
What do I **ask**? What kind? Which one? How many?
What do I **get**? An ADJECTIVE! (Clap) That's what!

Jingle 6: Article Adjective Jingle

We are the article adjectives,
Teeny, tiny adjectives:
A, AN, THE – A, AN, THE.

We are called article adjectives and noun markers;
We are memorized and used every day.
So, if you spot us, you can mark us
With the label A.

We are the article adjectives,
Teeny, tiny adjectives:
A, AN, THE – A, AN, THE.

Jingle Section

Jingle 7: Preposition Jingle

A PREP PREP PREPOSITION
Is a special group of words
That connects a
NOUN, NOUN, NOUN
Or a PRO PRO PRONOUN
To the rest of the sentence.

Jingle 8: Object of the Prep Jingle

Dum De Dum Dum!
An O-P is an N-O-U-N or a P-R-O
After the P-R-E-P
In an S-E-N-T-E-N-C-E.
Dum De Dum Dum - DONE!

Jingle 9: Pronoun

This little pronoun,
Floating around,
Takes the place of a little old noun.
With a knick knack paddy wack,
These are English rules.
Isn't language fun and cool?

Jingle 10: Subject Pronoun

There are seven subject pronouns
That are easy as can be:
I and we,   (clap two times)
He and she,   (clap two times)
It and they and you.   (clap three times)

Jingle 11: Possessive Pronoun

There are seven possessive pronouns
That are easy as can be:
My and our,   (clap two times)
His and her,   (clap two times)
Its and their and your.   (clap three times)

LEVEL 2

REFERENCE

SECTION

Reference Section

Reference 1: Study Skills

Get Organized . . .

1. <u>Be prepared!</u> Have pencils sharpened and supplies handy before you begin the day. Keep an assignment notebook. Record assignments, page numbers, and due dates.

2. <u>Organize your desk!</u> Each time you put something in it, know exactly where it goes. Avoid "stuffing." Start today by having a complete clean-out and fix-up. Put all folders and notebooks on one side of your desk and put all textbooks on the other side. Small items should be kept to the front in a zipper bag.

3. <u>Everything has a place!</u> Keep each subject in a separate folder so that you can find papers easily.

4. <u>Directions are important!</u> Take time to read and understand each direction even if you know what to do. Look at your teacher and concentrate on what he/she is saying.

5. <u>Proofread your work!</u> Check it over. Read everything you have written. Do your answers make sense? Have you skipped any problems?

Listen . . .

1. <u>Listen with your whole body!</u> Look right at the person who is talking. Turn your body toward the speaker and watch him as he speaks. Keep your legs and hands still. Try to be interested in what the person is saying. You will learn more, and you will also show that person that he/she is an important human being.

2. <u>Ask questions!</u> Try to understand what the person is saying. When the person says something you don't understand, raise your hand and wait to be called on. Remember to ask your question before your teacher gets busy with something else.

3. <u>Write it down!</u> Write down anything you think you might forget.

4. <u>Concentrate!</u> Save other thoughts for times when you are not listening. Think about what the person is saying. Listen with your brain as well as your ears.

5. <u>Listen to directions!</u> Listen to understand each step. Ask questions if you do not understand the directions.

Plan Your Time . . .

1. <u>Set goals for yourself!</u> Choose one study skill at a time that you need to improve. Think of reasons why you need help in this area. Make a list of the things you can do to improve. Then, stick to it.

2. <u>Plan your day!</u> Check your assignment folder every day. Know what you need to do and plan time to work on it. Check off completed assignments.

3. <u>Do what is important first!</u> Assignments that are due first should be completed first.

4. <u>Make each minute count!</u> Concentrate on the job at hand. If you don't waste time, you will have more time to do the things you like to do. Keep your eyes on your work and keep your pencil moving. Don't give yourself a chance to stop working by breaking your concentration.

5. <u>Reward yourself!</u> When you are able to complete a goal, allow yourself to feel proud for a job well-done. Reward yourself.

(Reference 1 is continued on the next page.)

Reference Section

Reference 1: Study Skills (continued)

Do Your Homework . . .

1. <u>Think before you leave school!</u> Check your assignment book and decide what you need to take home. Put books and folders you will need in a book bag.

2. <u>Schedule a time to study!</u> Think about your family's routine and decide on a good study time. Stick to your schedule.

3. <u>Study where you can concentrate!</u> You can get homework done in a very short time if you do it away from TV, conversations, etc., and without stopping for distractions. Have all supplies at your study area.

4. <u>Set a time limit to study!</u> See how long you can concentrate. You might use a timer to set a time to concentrate and then give yourself a break or a reward at the end of that time.

5. <u>Have a special place to keep homework!</u> When your homework is finished, put it in your book bag, and you will always have it ready to take to school.

Reference 2: Beginning Setup Plan for School

You should use this plan to keep things in order!

1. Have separate color-coded pocket folders for each subject.
2. Put unfinished work in the right-hand side and finished work in the left-hand side of each subject folder.
3. Put notes to study, graded tests, and study guides in the brads so you will have them to study for scheduled tests.
4. Have a trash folder to put all paper to be thrown away. If it doesn't belong in a folder, throw it away!
5. Have a paper folder to store extra clean sheets of paper. Keep it full at all times.
6. Have an assignment folder to be reviewed every day. (This is a very important folder. It must go home every night!)

Do these things and put them in your assignment folder

A. Keep a monthly calendar of homework assignments, test dates, report due dates, project due dates, meeting times, after-school activities, dates and times, review dates, etc.

B. Keep a grade sheet to record the grades received in each class. (You might also consider keeping your grades on the inside cover of each subject folder. However you keep your grades, just remember to keep up with them accurately. Your grades are your business, so keep up with them! Grades help you know what areas need attention.)

C. Make a list every day of the things you want to do so that you can keep track of what you finish and what you do not finish. Move the unfinished items to your new list the next day. (Yes, making this list takes some time, but it's your road map to success. You will always know at a glance what you set out to accomplish and what still needs to be done.)

7. If you have a locker, organize your locker, get rid of unnecessary papers; keep locker trips to a minimum. (There should be **no loose papers** in your locker!)
8. Keep all necessary school supplies in a handy, heavy-duty Ziploc bag or a pencil bag.

Reference Section

Reference 3A: Study Plan for School

You should check this plan every day!

1. Attend class regularly after eating breakfast to start your day.

2. Schoolwork is your job – make it an important part of your daily life.

3. Develop the "I'm-willing-to-do-what-it-takes-to-get-the-job-done" attitude.

4. Work with your teachers and parents to correct any attitudes or habits that keep you from learning.

5. Make the effort to really listen, ask questions if you don't understand, and answer questions if asked.

6. Write it down! Write it down! Write it down! Make taking notes in class a habit. Then, put them in the correct folder.

7. Ask about make-up work and turn it in on time.

8. Turn your daily assignments in on time.

9. Check your assignment folder every day. Know what is on your calendar. Remember to record everything on your calendar so you won't get behind!

10. Concentrate on the job at hand. If you don't waste time, you will have a chance to finish your work. Keep your eyes on your work and keep your pencil moving. Don't give yourself a chance to stop working by breaking your concentration. Every time your eyes leave your paper to look around, you lose working time.

11. Do what is important first! Assignments that are due first should be completed first.

12. Think before you leave school! Check your assignment folder and decide what you need to take home. Put books and folders you will need in a book bag so you won't forget them.

Reference Section

Reference 3B: Study Plan for Home

Stick to this plan every evening!

1. Schedule a time to study. Think about your family's routine and decide on a good study time. Stick to your schedule.

2. Study where you can concentrate. Sorry! No TV or telephone while you study! (Get your studying job finished and then watch TV or talk on the telephone, if you must. Remember, TV does not get you ahead in life – education will!)

3. Make a personal decision to concentrate 100 percent on completing your homework assignments. You will get more accomplished in less time with 100 percent concentration than if you give 25 percent of your concentration for a longer period of time.

4. Check your assignment folder every day. Get control of your life!

5. Have a special place to keep homework. When your homework is finished, put it in your book bag right then, and you will always have it ready to take to school, no matter how hassled your morning is.

6. Use your home study time to do your assignments or to review for a test. Don't wait until the last minute to study for a test. Study a little every night so that you won't overload the night before. (And, of course, you'll probably have company the night before the big test! That's why you don't wait until the last minute to study – take charge!)

7. If possible, set a weekly meeting time to discuss your progress with your parents. If it is not possible, meet with yourself. You need to discuss your progress and problems. See which study skill you did not follow. Figure out what to do to "fix" it, and try again! You'll get better with practice.

8. You are old enough to help yourself! Remember, school is your business, your job, and your responsibility.

Reference 4: Synonyms and Antonyms

Directions: Underline the **syn** if the words are synonyms. Underline the **ant** if the words are antonyms.

1. warm, hot	**syn** ant	2. high, low	syn **ant**	3. chilly, cold	**syn** ant

---

Reference 5: Two Kinds of Sentences and the End Mark Flow

1. A **declarative** sentence makes a statement. It is labeled with a **D**.
Example: Bill walked to town.
(Period, statement, declarative sentence)

2. An **interrogative** sentence asks a question. It is labeled with an ***Int***.
Example: Are you leaving tomorrow?
(Question mark, question, interrogative sentence)

Examples: Read each sentence, recite the end mark flow in parentheses, and put the end mark and abbreviation at the end of the sentence.

1. I went to town yesterday **. D**
(Period, statement, declarative sentence)

2. Did you go to the ballgame **? Int**
(Question mark, question, interrogative sentence)

Reference Section

Reference 6: What is Journal Writing?

Journal Writing is a written record of your personal thoughts and feelings about things or people that are important to you. Recording your thoughts in a journal is a good way to remember how you felt about what was happening in your life at a particular time. You can record your dreams, memories, feelings, and experiences. You can ask questions and answer some of them. It is fun to go back later and read what you have written because it shows how you have changed in different areas of your life.

What do I write about?

Journals are personal, but sometimes it helps to have ideas to get you started. Remember, in a journal, you do not have to stick to one topic. Write about someone or something in school. Write about what you did last weekend or on vacation. Write about what you hope to do this week or on your next vacation. Write about home, school, friends, enemies, hobbies, special talents (yours or someone else's), present and future hopes and fears. Write about what is wrong in your world and what you would do to "fix" it. Write about the good things and the bad things in your world. If you think about a past event and want to write an opinion about it now, put it in your journal. If you want to give your opinion about a present or future event that could have an impact on your life or the way you see things, put it in your journal. If something bothers you, record it in your journal. If something interests you, record it. If you just want to record something that doesn't seem important at all, write it in your journal. After all, it is your journal!

How do I get started writing in my personal journal?

You need to put the day's date on the title line of your paper: **Month, Day, Year.** Skip the next line and begin your entry. You might write one or two sentences, a paragraph, a whole page, or several pages. Except for the journal date, no particular organizational style is required for journal writing. You decide how best to organize and express your thoughts. Feel free to include drawings, lists, etc., if they will help you remember your thoughts about a topic or an event. You will also need a spiral notebook, a pen or pencil, a quiet place, and at least 5-10 minutes of uninterrupted writing time.

Reference 7: Practice Sentence

Labels:	A	Adj	Adj	SN	V	Adv	Adv
Practice:	**The**	**two**	**smart**	**firemen**	**moved**	**quickly**	**away.**

Reference 8: Improved Sentence

Labels:	A	Adj	Adj	SN	V	Adv	Adv
Practice:	The	two	smart	firemen	moved	quickly	away.
Improved:	**The**	**five**	**expert**	**firemen**	**dashed**	**rapidly**	**ahead.**
	(same word)	(word change)	(synonym)	(same word)	(synonym)	(synonym)	(word change)

Reference Section

| Reference 9: Sample Vocabulary Words for Practice and Improved Sentences ||||||
Nouns	Verbs	Adjectives	Adverbs	Prepositions	Pronouns
boys, girls, firemen, sailor, train, ship, cars, horse, squirrel, grandmother, mother, father, monkeys, cats, flowers, stars	laughed raced scampered sailed danced grew climbed slept	a, an, the young huge three friendly delicious happy sleepy	quietly quickly happily today loudly slowly gracefully yesterday	across around down, during in, at on to under with	I, we he, she it they, you my, our his, her its their, your

Reference 10: Noun Job

```
        A    Adj  Adj     SN       V      Adv    Adv
5.      The  five  sad  students  /  walked  slowly  away.  D
```

Directions: Underline the complete subject once and the complete predicate twice in Sentence 5 above. Then, complete the table below.

List the Noun Used	List the Noun Job	Singular or Plural	Common or Proper	Simple Subject	Simple Predicate
students	SN	P	C	students	walked

Reference 11: One Part of Speech

Finding One Part of Speech. For each sentence, write **SN** above the simple subject and **V** above the simple predicate. Underline the word(s) for the part of speech listed to the left of each sentence.

Adjective(s):

```
              SN    V
1. The old chair broke yesterday.
```

Adverb(s):

```
              SN    V
2. The yellow bee buzzed loudly.
```

Noun(s):

```
              SN    V
3. Two black cars raced yesterday.
```

Verb(s):

```
      SN      V
4. Grandma slept peacefully.
```

Reference Section

Reference 12: The Topic

Finding the topic: Write the name of the topic that best describes what each row of words is about. Choose from these topics: Colors, Clothing, Toys, or Animals.

(1) __Clothing__	(2) __Animals__	(3) __Colors__
dress	tiger	black
shirt	lion	red
sweater	zebra	orange
pants	giraffe	yellow

Reference 13: Supporting and Non-Supporting Ideas and Sentences

Words that support the topic: In each row, cross out the one idea that does not support the underlined topic at the top.

(1) Food	(2) Transportation	(3) School Supplies
pizza	car	pencil
apple	bus	~~dog~~
hamburger	~~green~~	glue
cheese	boat	crayons
~~book~~	jet	scissors

Sentences that support the topic: Read the topic. Then, cross out the one sentence that does not support the topic.

Topic: A Funny-Looking Clown

1. The circus clown wore red baggy pants.
2. The clown's green hair stuck straight out.
3. ~~I like clowns and acrobats.~~
4. Floppy old shoes made the clown walk funny.

Reference Section

Reference 14: Two-Point Expository Paragraph Example

Topic: **Favorite colors**
Two main points: 1. **blue**   2. **green**

Sentence #1 – <u>Topic Sentence</u> (*Use words in the topic and tell how many points will be used.*)
I have two favorite colors.

Sentence #2 – <u>2-Point Sentence</u> (*List the 2 points in the order you will present them.*)
These colors are blue and green.

Sentence #3 – <u>First Point</u>
My first favorite color is blue.

Sentence #4 – <u>Supporting Sentence</u> for the first point.
I like blue because it reminds me of a beautiful summer sky.

Sentence #5 – <u>Second Point</u>
My second favorite color is green.

Sentence #6 – <u>Supporting Sentence</u> for the second point.
I like green shirts because I look good in green.

Sentence #7 – <u>Concluding (final) Sentence</u>. (*Restate the topic sentence and add an extra thought.*)
My two favorite colors make me feel warm and happy inside.

SAMPLE PARAGRAPH   **My Favorite Colors**

   I have two favorite colors. These colors are blue and green. My first favorite color is blue. I like blue because it reminds me of a beautiful summer sky. My second favorite color is green. I like green shirts because I look good in green. My two favorite colors make me feel warm and happy inside.

General Checklist: Check the Finished Paragraph	**The Two-Point Expository Paragraph Outline**
(1) Have you followed the pattern for a 2-point paragraph? (*Indent, topic sentence, 2-point sentence, 2 main points, 2 supporting sentences, and a concluding sentence.*)	Topic 2 points about the topic Sentence #1: **Topic** sentence Sentence #2: A **two-point** sentence
(2) Do you have complete sentences?	Sentence #3: A **first point** sentence Sentence #4: A **supporting** sentence for the first point
(3) Have you capitalized the first word and put an end mark at the end of every sentence?	Sentence #5: A **second point** sentence Sentence #6: A **supporting** sentence for the second point
(4) Have you checked your sentences for capitalization and punctuation mistakes?	Sentence #7: A **concluding** sentence

Reference Section

Reference 15: Paragraph for Singular and Plural Points

Two-Point Expository Paragraph

Topic: My favorite large animals
2-points: 1. elephants 2. polar bears

   I have two favorite large animals. These animals are elephants and polar bears. My first favorite large animal is an elephant. I like elephants because they live in peaceful family units. My second favorite large animal is a polar bear. The polar bear has a beautiful white coat that blends with the snow in the polar regions. My two favorite animals are very interesting, and I enjoy learning as much as I can about each one of them.

Reference 16: Knowing the Difference Between Prepositions and Adverbs

           Adv
In the sample sentence, *Dan fell **down***, the word *down* is an adverb because it does not have a noun after it.
       P   noun (OP)
In the sample sentence, *Dan fell **down the hill***, the word *down* is a preposition because it has the noun *hill* (the object of the preposition) after it. To find the preposition and object of the preposition in the question and answer flow, say:

down - P   (Say: *down - preposition*)
down what? hill - OP (Say: *down what? hill - object of the preposition*)

Reference 17: Noun Job With a Preposition

   A Adj Adj SN V P A OP
1. The two tall boys / walked (down the path.) **D**

Directions: Underline the complete subject once and the complete predicate twice in Sentence 1 above. Then, complete the table below.

List the Noun Used	List the Noun Job	Singular or Plural	Common or Proper	Simple Subject	Simple Predicate
boys	SN	P	C	boys	walked
path	OP	S	C		

Reference Section

Reference 18: Capitalization Rules

1. Capitalize the first word of a sentence.
2. Capitalize the pronoun I.
3. Capitalize the names of people and the names of pets. (*Joe, Buffy*)
4. Capitalize titles used with people's names and people's initials. (*Mr., Aunt, Dr., J. C.*)
5. Capitalize names of streets, cities, states, and countries. (*Oak Street, Dallas, Texas, France*)
6. Capitalize the days of the week and the months of the year. (*Monday, May*)

Example:

1(or4) 3		2	6	5	(Rule numbers)
M T		I	F	J	

1. mr. tom and i left on friday for japan.   **(Editing Guide: 5 capitalization mistakes)**

Reference 19: Punctuation Rules

1. Use a period after initials. (*L. C. Jones*).
2. Use a period after an abbreviation. (*Dr., Feb., Mr.*)
3. Use a comma to separate the city from the state. (*Dallas, Texas*)
4. Use a comma between the day and the year. (*July 4, 1998*)
5. Put a period or question mark at the end of a sentence.

Example:

1(or 4) 4 4 3		5	5	(Rule numbers)
M J C S		D	C	

1. mr. j. c. smith drove to denver, colorado.   **(Editing Guide: 6 capitals & 5 punctuation)**

  2   1   1   3   5   (Rule numbers)

Reference 20: Possessive Nouns

1. A possessive noun is the name of a person, place, or thing that owns something.
2. A possessive noun will always have an apostrophe after it. It will be either an *apostrophe s ('s)* or an *s apostrophe (s')*. The apostrophe makes a noun show ownership. (*Brian's coat*)
3. A possessive noun's main job is to show ownership or possession.
4. Use the abbreviation **PN** (possessive noun).
5. Include possessive nouns when you are asked to identify possessive nouns or adjectives. Do not include possessive nouns when you are asked to identify regular nouns.
6. To find a possessive noun, begin with the question *whose*. (*Whose coat? Brian's - PN*)

Reference Section

PRESENT	PAST	PAST PARTICIPLE	PRESENT PARTICIPLE
become	became	(has) become	(is) becoming
begin	began	(has) begun	(is) beginning
blow	blew	(has) blown	(is) blowing
break	broke	(has) broken	(is) breaking
bring	brought	(has) brought	(is) bringing
burst	burst	(has) burst	(is) bursting
buy	bought	(has) bought	(is) buying
choose	chose	(has) chosen	(is) choosing
come	came	(has) come	(is) coming
do	did	(has) done	(is) doing
drink	drank	(has) drunk	(is) drinking
drive	drove	(has) driven	(is) driving
eat	ate	(has) eaten	(is) eating
fall	fell	(has) fallen	(is) falling
fly	flew	(has) flown	(is) flying
freeze	froze	(has) frozen	(is) freezing
get	got	(has) gotten	(is) getting
give	gave	(has) given	(is) giving
go	went	(has) gone	(is) going
grow	grew	(has) grown	(is) growing
know	knew	(has) known	(is) knowing
lie	lay	(has) lain	(is) lying
lay	laid	(has) laid	(is) laying
make	made	(has) made	(is) making
ride	rode	(has) ridden	(is) riding
ring	rang	(has) rung	(is) ringing
rise	rose	(has) risen	(is) rising
run	ran	(has) run	(is) running
see	saw	(has) seen	(is) seeing
sell	sold	(has) sold	(is) selling
sing	sang	(has) sung	(is) singing
sink	sank	(has) sunk	(is) sinking
set	set	(has) set	(is) setting
sit	sat	(has) sat	(is) sitting
shoot	shot	(has) shot	(is) shooting
swim	swam	(has) swum	(is) swimming
take	took	(has) taken	(is) taking
tell	told	(has) told	(is) telling
throw	threw	(has) thrown	(is) throwing
wear	wore	(has) worn	(is) wearing
write	wrote	(has) written	(is) writing

Reference 21: Verb Chant Chart for Irregular Verbs

Reference Section

Reference 22: Subject-Verb Agreement Rules

Rule 1: A singular subject must use a singular verb form that ends in **s**: *is, was, has, does, or verbs ending with* **s** *or* **es.**
Rule 2: A plural subject or the subject **YOU** must use a plural verb form that has **no s** ending:
are, were, do, have, or verbs without **s** *or* **es** *endings.* (A plural verb form is also called the *plain form.*)

Directions: For each sentence, write the subject, then write **S** if the subject is singular or **P** if the subject is plural, write the rule number, and underline the correct verb in the sentence.

Subject	S or P	Rule
dog	S	1
dogs	P	2
dog	S	1
boys	P	2
boy	S	1
You	P	2

Examples
1. The angry dog (bark, <u>barks</u>) loudly at the cat.
2. The angry dogs (<u>bark</u>, barks) loudly at the cat.
3. The angry dog (<u>was</u>, were) barking loudly at the cat.
4. The boys (was, <u>were</u>) going to the park.
5. The boy (<u>was</u>, were) going to the park.
6. You (<u>work</u>, works) at your desk.

Reference 23: Complete Sentences and Sentence Fragments

Identifying simple sentences and fragments: Write **S** for a complete sentence and **F** for a sentence fragment on the line beside each group of words below.

S	1.	The birds sang sweetly.
F	2.	In the world.
S	3.	Two lions walk to the water.
S	4.	Ducks quacked.
F	5.	Bark at the children.
F	6.	The huge rocks.

Reference 24: Matching Subject Parts and Predicate Parts

Match each subject part with the correct predicate part by writing the correct sentence number in the blank.

1. The hungry monkey
2. The big airplane
3. The artist
4. The funny clowns
5. The wet snow

5	made a good snowman.
1	ate several bananas.
4	do tricks for the children.
2	flies high in the sky.
3	drew a pretty picture.

Reference 25: Correcting Sentence Fragments

Directions: On your own paper, make each fragment below into a complete sentence. Underline the parts you add.

1. Add a subject part to this fragment: **ran after the car.**
   <u>**The big angry dog**</u> **ran after the car.**

2. Add a predicate part to this fragment: **The teacher.**
   The teacher <u>**gave the final directions for the treasure hunt**</u>**.**

Reference Section

Reference 26: Descriptive Writing Guidelines

1. **When describing people,** it is helpful to notice these types of details: How they look, how they walk, or how they talk, their way of doing things, any special event that happened to the person being described, and any other details that will help make that person stand out in your mind.

2. **When describing places or things,** it is helpful to notice these types of details: What you can see, smell, or touch about a place or thing (*includes color, shape, size, age*), any other unusual information about a place or thing, any special event that happened in the place or thing being described, and whether or not the place or thing is special to you.

3. **When describing nature,** it is helpful to notice these types of details: The special part or quality of the season, the sights, smells, sounds, colors, animals, insects, birds, and any special happening related to the scene being described.

4. **When describing an incident or an event,** it is helpful to notice these types of details: The order in which the event takes place, any specific facts that will keep the story moving from a beginning to an ending, the answers to any of the *who, what, when, where, why*, and *how* questions that the reader needs to know, and especially the details that will create a clear picture, such as how things look, sound, smell, feel, etc.

Reference 27: Descriptive Paragraph Example

A. Sentence 1 is the topic sentence that introduces **what is being described.**

B. For Sentences 2-5, use **the descriptive details** in Reference 26.

C. Sentence 6 is a concluding sentence that **restates or relates back to the topic sentence.**

Noisy Country Sounds

We live in the peaceful country, but it sure isn't quiet. In fact, it gets downright noisy! As we settle down for a quiet, summer evening, the crickets and frogs start their lively concert. They play loud and long. The dark green frogs harmonize their voices with the chirping sound made by the skinny little crickets as they strum their violins. There is nothing like country noise, and you either hate it or love it.

Reference Section

Reference 28: Contraction Chart						
Column 1		**Column 2**		**Column 3**		
Verb Meaning	Contraction	Verb Meaning	Contraction	Pronoun	Contraction	
AM		HAS				
I am	— I'm	has not	— hasn't	**its**	**it's**	
		he has	— he's	(owns)	(it is)	
IS		she has	— she's	*its hair*	*it's damp*	
is not	— isn't					
he is	— he's	HAVE				
she is	— she's	have not	— haven't	**your**	**you're**	
it is	— it's	I have	— I've	(owns)	(you are)	
who is	— who's	you have	— you've	*your dog*	*you're going*	
that is	— that's	we have	— we've			
what is	— what's	they have	— they've			
there is	— there's			**their**	**they're**	
		HAD		(owns)	(they are)	
ARE		had not	— hadn't	*their car*	*they're happy*	
are not	— aren't	I had	— I'd			
you are	— you're	he had	— he'd			
we are	— we're	she had	— she'd	**whose**	**who's**	
they are	— they're	you had	— you'd	(owns)	(who is)	
		we had	— we'd	*whose hat*	*who's talking*	
WAS, WERE		they had	— they'd			
was not	— wasn't					
were not	— weren't	WILL /SHALL				
		will not	— won't			
DO, DOES, DID		I will	— I'll			
do not	— don't	he will	— he'll			
does not	— doesn't	she will	— she'll			
did not	— didn't	you will	— you'll			
		we will	— we'll			
CAN		they will	— they'll			
cannot	— can't					
		WOULD				
LET		would not	— wouldn't			
let us	— let's	I would	— I'd			
		he would	— he'd			
		she would	— she'd			
		you would	— you'd			
		we would	— we'd			
		they would	— they'd			
		SHOULD, COULD				
		should not	— shouldn't			
		could not	— couldn't			

Reference Section

Reference 29: A and An Choices

Rule 1: Use the word **a** when the next word begins with a consonant sound. (*Example: a golden orange.*)
Rule 2: Use the word **an** when the next word begins with a vowel sound. (*Example: an orange.*)

Sample Sentences: Write **a** or **an** in the blanks.

1. Would you like __an__ apple?   3. We saw __a__ pumpkin.
2. Would you like __a__ red apple?   4. We saw __an__ orange pumpkin.

Reference 30: Story Elements Outline

1. **Main Idea (Tell the problem or situation that needs a solution.)**
   Joey's new puppy keeps chewing up the family's shoes.

2. **Setting (Tell when and where the story takes place, either clearly stated or implied.)**
   When - The story takes place over a period of a week.   Where - The story takes place at Joey's house.

3. **Character (Tell who or what the story is about.)**
   The main characters are Joey, his parents, Mr. and Mrs. Arnold, and his teenage sister, Kim.

4. **Plot (Tell what the characters in the story do and what happens to them.)**
   The story is about Joey finally getting a new puppy. The puppy chews and destroys four pairs of shoes in less than a week. Joey's parents threaten to get rid of the puppy.

5. **Ending (Use a strong ending that will bring the story to a close.)**
   The story ends with Joey buying the new puppy some chew toys and a puppy kennel to keep him in when he can't be supervised.

The Destructo Dog

Joey was so excited when his dad brought home a new puppy on Sunday. It had taken him a long time to show his parents that he could take care of a puppy. Joey named his dog Dandy. Everyone in the family enjoyed Dandy the first day. Then, things began to fall apart. During the week while everyone was away at school and work, Dandy began helping himself to shoes. First, he chewed Mom's sandals. Next, he chewed Dad's boots and Joey's sneakers. The final straw was when Dandy chewed Kim's prom shoes! At the family meeting, Mr. Arnold said that Dandy had to go. But when Joey offered to use money he had saved to buy a dog kennel and some chew toys, Mr. and Mrs. Arnold agreed to give Dandy another chance. Keeping him in the kennel and giving him his own things to chew might make him a dandy dog after all!

Reference Section

Reference 31: Present, Past, and Future Verb Tenses

When you are writing paragraphs, you must use verbs that are in the same tense. Tense means time. The tense of a verb shows the time of the action. There are three basic tenses that show when an action takes place. They are **present tense, past tense,** and **future tense**. Now, you will learn to recognize each kind of tense.

1. The **present tense** shows that something is happening now, in the present. Present tense verbs that are singular end in **-s**, or **-es**. Present tense verbs that are plural do not end in **-s**, or **-es**.
   (Singular present tense verb: listens) (Plural present tense verb: listen)

   (**Examples:** The student <u>listens</u> carefully. The students <u>listen</u> carefully.)

2. The **past tense** shows that something has happened sometime in the past. Most past tense verbs end in **-ed** for both the singular and plural forms.
   (Singular past tense verb: listened) (Plural past tense verb: listened)

   (**Examples:** The student <u>listened</u> carefully. The students <u>listened</u> carefully.)

3. The **future tense** shows that something will happen sometime in the future. The future tense form always has the helping verb *will or shall* before the main verb for both the singular and plural forms.
   (Singular future tense verb: will listen) (Plural future tense verb: will listen)

   (**Examples:** The student <u>will listen</u> carefully. The students <u>will listen</u> carefully.)

Present Tense	Past Tense	Future Tense
What to look for: **one verb** with -s, -es, or *plain ending*.	What to look for: **one verb** with -ed.	What to look for: **will** or **shall** with a main verb.
The baby <u>cries</u> for his bottle.	The baby <u>cried</u> for his bottle.	The baby <u>will cry</u> for his bottle.

Test Example: Identify the tense of each underlined verb by writing a number **1** for present tense, a number **2** for past tense, or a number **3** for future tense.

Verb Tense	Verbs	Verb Tense	Verbs
1	1. She <u>cheers</u> at the football game.	3	4. The principal <u>will talk</u> to our class.
2	2. She <u>cheered</u> at the football game.	1	5. The principal <u>talks</u> to our class.
3	3. She <u>will cheer</u> at the football game.	2	6. The principal <u>talked</u> to our class.

Reference Section

Reference 32: Regular and Irregular Verbs

All verbs can be changed to past tense. The way you change a verb to past tense will make it a regular or irregular verb.

Regular Verbs: As you have just learned, you add *-ed* to most verbs to form the past tense. Verbs that are made past tense by adding *-ed* are called **regular verbs**. Most verbs are regular verbs because they form their past tense by adding *-ed*.

Irregular Verbs: However, a few verbs, like the verbs on the verb chant chart, are made past tense by a spelling change. The verbs from the verb chant chart are called **irregular verbs**. The only way to learn how to write and speak using irregular verbs is to memorize them. But for now, you can just use the verb chant chart.

1. **Regular and irregular present tense verbs:**
   (Regular present tense verbs: listen, listens) (Irregular present tense verbs from the verb chant chart: grow, grows)

   (**Examples:** The students listen carefully. Flowers grow along the drive.)

2. **Regular and irregular past tense verbs:**
   (Regular past tense verbs: listened) (Irregular past tense verbs from the verb chant chart: grew)

   (**Examples:** The students listened to their teacher. Flowers grew along the drive.)

3. **Regular and irregular future tense verbs:**
   (Regular future tense form: will listen) (Irregular future tense verbs from the verb chant chart: will grow)

   (**Examples:** The students will listen carefully. Flowers will grow along the drive.)

Present Tense	Past Tense	Future Tense
What to look for: **one verb** with *-s, -es,* or *plain ending*.	What to look for: **one verb** with *-ed* or an irregular spelling word.	What to look for: **will** or **shall** with a main verb.
1. The baby cries for his bottle. 2. The baby drinks his milk.	3. The baby cried for his bottle. 4. The baby drank his milk.	5. The baby will cry for his bottle. 6. The baby will drink his milk.

Test Example: Identify the tense of each underlined verb by writing a number **1** for present tense, a number **2** for past tense, or a number **3** for future tense. Use the verb chant chart for the irregular verbs.

Verb Tense	Regular Verbs	Verb Tense	Irregular Verbs
1	1. We walk to school.	1	4. The geese fly south.
2	2. We walked to school.	2	5. The geese flew south.
3	3. We will walk to school.	3	6. The geese will fly south.

Reference Section

Reference 33: Homonym Chart

Homonyms are words which sound the same but have different meanings and different spellings.

1. **buy** - to purchase	9. **our** - belonging to us	17. **their** - belonging to them
2. **by** - at, near	10. **hour** - sixty minutes	18. **there** - in that place
3. **hear** - to listen	11. **peace** - quiet	19. **they're** - they are
4. **here** - in this place	12. **piece** - a part	20. **to** - toward, (preposition)
5. **its** - possessive pronoun	13. **right** - correct	21. **too** - also
6. **it's** - it is	14. **write** - to form letters	22. **two** - a couple
7. **knew** - understood	15. **weak** - not strong	23. **your** - belonging to you
8. **new** - not old	16. **week** - seven days	24. **you're** - you are

Examples: Underline the correct homonym.

1. My brother has (**weak**, week) ankles.   2. He has a (weak, **week**) to complete the assignment.

Reference 34: Time-Order Paragraph Examples

A time-order paragraph means that the sentences are in an order that makes sense. You should also use words that suggest a definite number order, such as *first, second, third*, etc. or *first, next, last* or *finally*.

Example 1:   **A Pig Party**

Topic: My pig party   **3-points:** 1. costume contest   2. pig lunch   3. pin the tail on the pig

    Saturday, I had a pig party at my house. <u>First</u>, we had a contest to see who could dress up in the best pig costume. Katie won because she dressed like Miss Piggy. <u>Second</u>, we ate a lunch of pigs-in-the-blanket. The table was decorated like a pig trough. <u>Third</u>, we had fun playing pin the curly tail on the pig. The prize was a jar of candy pigs! Everyone had a great time at my pig party!

Example 2:   **A Pig Party**

Topic: My pig party   **3-points:** 1. costume contest   2. pig lunch   3. pin the tail on the pig

    Saturday, I had a pig party at my house. <u>First</u>, we had a contest to see who could dress up in the best pig costume. Katie won because she dressed like Miss Piggy. <u>Next</u>, we ate a lunch of pigs-in-the-blanket. The table was decorated like a pig trough. <u>Last</u>, we had fun playing pin the curly tail on the pig. The prize was a jar of candy pigs! Everyone had a great time at my pig party!

Example 3:   **How to Eat an Apple**

Topic: How to eat an apple **3-points:** 1. wash it   2. cut and core it   3. spread peanut butter on it

    I love to eat delicious apples. <u>First</u>, I wash and dry my apple. I want to make sure it is clean and germ-free. <u>Next</u>, Mom cuts it in fourths and removes the core. I let her help me so I won't cut myself. <u>Last</u>, I spread peanut butter on each piece. I think peanut butter on apples tastes great! Fixing and eating my own tasty apple snack makes me feel grown-up.

Reference Section

Reference 35: The Time-Order Paragraph Pattern

Topic: My Pig Party **Points:** 1. costume contest   2. pig lunch   3. pin the tail on the pig

Topic Sentence

1st point   (The first thing that happens. Use this time word: **First**.)
Supporting sentence

2nd point   (The second thing that happens. Use these time words: **Second or Next**.)
Supporting sentence

3rd point   (The third thing that happens. Use these time words: **Third, Last, or Finally**.)
Supporting sentence

Conclusion

General Checklist: Check the Finished Paragraph

(1) Have you followed the pattern for a time-order paragraph?
    (*Indent, topic sentence, 3 main points, 3 supporting sentences, and a concluding sentence.*)

(2) Do you have complete sentences?

(3) Have you capitalized the first word and put an end mark at the end of every sentence?

(4) Have you checked your sentences for capitalization and punctuation mistakes?

Reference 36: Tips for Writing Friendly Letters

Tip #1: Write as if you were talking to the person face-to-face. Share information about yourself and mutual friends. Tell stories, conversations, or jokes. Share photographs, articles, drawings, poems, etc. Avoid saying something about someone else that you'll be sorry for later.

Tip #2: If you are writing a return letter, be sure to answer any questions that were asked. Repeat the question so that your reader will know what you are writing about. (You asked about . . .)

Tip #3: End your letter in a positive way so that your reader will want to write a return letter.

Reference Section

Reference 37: Friendly Letter Example

1. Heading
Write your address.
Write the date.

27 Park Lane
Jackson, AR 72023
March 3, 20____

2. Friendly Greeting, (or Salutation)
Name the person receiving the letter.
Use a comma.

Dear Susan,

3. Body (Indent Paragraphs)
Write what you want to say. Indent.

I can't wait until you come next week. We will swim and play with my new puppies. See you then.

4. Closing
Capitalize the first word.
Use a comma.

Your friend,

5. Signature
Sign your name.

Marie

Reference 38: The Five Parts of a Friendly Letter

1. Heading
1. Box or street address of writer
2. City, state, zip code of writer
3. Date letter was written
4. Placement: upper right hand corner

2. Friendly Greeting or Salutation
1. Begins with *Dear*
2. Names person receiving the letter
3. Has comma after person's name
4. Placement: at left margin, two lines below heading

3. Body
1. Tells reason the letter was written
2. Can have one or more paragraphs
3. Has indented paragraphs
4. Is placed one line after the greeting
5. Skips one line between each paragraph

4. Closing
1. Closes letter with a personal phrase-(Your friend, With love,)
2. Capitalizes only first word
3. Is followed by a comma
4. Is placed two lines below the body
5. Begins just to the right of the middle of the letter

5. Signature
1. Tells who wrote the letter
2. Is usually signed in cursive
3. Uses first name only unless there is a question as to which friend or relative you are
4. Is placed beneath the closing

Reference Section

Reference 39: Envelope Parts	Friendly Envelope Example
The return address: 1. Name of the person writing the letter 2. Box or street address of the writer 3. City, state, zip code of the writer **The mailing address:** 1. Name of the person receiving the letter 2. Street address of the person receiving the letter 3. City, state, zip of the person receiving the letter	**Return Address** Write your name and address. Marie Jones 27 Park Lane Jackson, AR 72023 Stamp **Mailing Address** Write the name & address of the person receiving the letter. Susan Day 28 Vise Lane Jones, Texas 76830

Reference 40: Thank-You Note for a Gift

For a Gift

What -	Thank you for... (tell color, kind, and item)
Use -	Tell how the gift is used.
Thanks -	I appreciate your thinking of me at this time.

Example 1: Gift

Heading
11 Vine Street
Rose, Texas 77123
June 30, 20___

Greeting
Dear Aunt Jane,

Body
Thank you for the gloves you sent for my birthday. They will keep me warm. I like your gift because it reminds me of you.

Closing
Your niece,

Signature
Tammy

Reference Section

Reference 41: Thank-You Note for an Action

<u>**For an Action**</u>

What -	Thank you for...
	(tell action)
Use -	Tell how the action helped.
Thanks -	I appreciate your remembering me.

Example 2: Action

Heading
6 James Circle
Tinytown, Florida 21107
July 1, 20___

Greeting
Dear Kay,

      Body
Thank you for helping when Daddy was in the hospital. Babysitting us really helped a lot. We appreciate your kindness.

Closing
Your friend,

Signature
Laura

Reference 42: Alphabetical Order

Example: Put each group of words in alphabetical order. Use numbers to show the order in each column.

Color Words		"B" Words		Shape Words		Math Words		"W" Words	
2	1. yellow	1	3. banana	2	5. square	2	7. subtract	1	9. wall
1	2. brown	2	4. boy	1	6. circle	1	8. add	2	10. winter

Reference Section

Reference 43: The Dictionary

1. The words listed in a dictionary are called entry words and are in bold face type.

2. The entry words are listed in alphabetical order (ABC order).

3. The dictionary tells how to spell a word and how to pronounce a word.

4. The dictionary tells what the word means and gives an example to explain a meaning.

5. The dictionary tells how to use the word and gives the part(s) of speech for a word.

Dictionary Entry Words

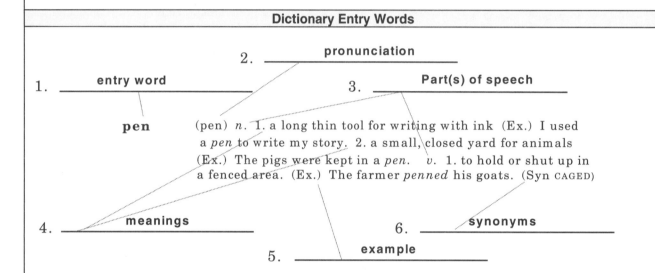

Parts of a Dictionary Entry

1. The entry word – gives correct spelling and divides the word into syllables.

2. Pronunciation – tells how to pronounce a word. It is usually put in parentheses.

3. Parts of speech – use a small *n.* for noun, a small *v.* for verb, an *adj.* for adjective, etc.

4. Meanings – are numbered definitions listed according to the part of speech.

5. Example – is a sentence using the entry word to explain a meaning. (Shown as *Ex.*)

6. Synonyms – are words that have similar meanings to the entry word. (Shown as *Syn*)

Guidelines for Dictionary Entry Words

1. Put words in ABC order.

2. Give a meaning for each word.

3. Write a sentence using the word.

4. Draw a picture about the word.

Reference Section

Reference 44: Parts of a Book

AT THE FRONT:

1. **Title Page.** This page has the full title of the book, the author's name, the illustrator's name, the publishing company, and the city where the book was published.

2. **Copyright Page.** This page is right after the title page and tells the year in which the book was published and who owns the copyright. If the book has an ISBN number (International Standard Book Number), it is listed here.

3. **Table of Contents.** This section lists the major divisions of the book by units or chapters and tells their page numbers.

4. **Body.** This is the main section or text of the book.

AT THE BACK:

5. **Glossary.** This section is like a dictionary and gives the meanings of some of the important words in the book.

6. **Bibliography.** This section gives a list of books used by the author. It could serve as a guide for further reading on a topic.

7. **Index.** This will probably be your most useful section. The purpose of the index is to help you quickly locate information about the topics in the book. It has an alphabetical list of specific topics and tells on which page that information can be found. It is similar to the table of contents, but it is much more detailed.

Reference 45: Reading Speed

REASONS FOR READING:	READING SPEED:
1. **To enjoy** yourself	**Read slowly** enough to enjoy the story.
2. **To understand** main ideas and details . . .	**Read slowly** so you can stop and think about what is being said.
3. **To get an idea** about the topic	**Read quickly**, looking for titles, topic headings, underlining, and words in bold type.
4. **To locate answers** to specific questions . . .	**Read quickly**, looking for titles, topic headings, underlining, and words in bold type to find the key words in your question. **Then, read slowly** to find the answers to your specific questions.

Reference Section

Reference 46: How to Read Subject Matter Material

Step 1. **SKIM – done quickly to get a general idea of the article.**

Look quickly over titles, topic headings, topic sentences for each paragraph, and underlining or boldface type. <u>Your purpose is to get an idea of the topic</u>. This is called <u>skimming</u>.

Step 2. **QUESTION – turn headings into questions to get a purpose for reading.**

Some headings are written as questions. You have to turn other headings into questions. <u>These heading questions will give you a reason for reading</u>. You are more likely to pick out and remember the main facts when you are looking for answers to questions.

Step 3. **READ – done slowly to find and understand details about topic headings.**

<u>The purpose</u> of this step is to read slow enough <u>to get complete answers</u> to the questions you asked in the question step. Read carefully <u>to understand and remember the main ideas</u> and details of the article.

Step 4. **SCAN – done quickly to relocate specific answers to study questions.**

Quickly look over titles, topic headings, and underlining or boldface type. <u>The purpose is to locate specific answers to study questions from your book or worksheet</u>. This is called scanning.
